G000270843

THE
SYLVAC
COLLECTORS HANDBOOK
Part 2

By Anthony Van Der Woerd
Georgian Publications
PO Box 1449,
Bath, BA1 2FF

ISBN 0 9521811 18

Important Notice

All information in this book has been compiled from reliable sources and every effort has been made to eliminate errors and questionable data. Nevertheless, the possibility of a mistake always exists. The author cannot, accordingly be held responsible for losses which may occur in the purchase, sale or other transactions by reason of any information contained herein or indirectly attributable to the contents of this work. Readers who feel they have discovered errors or would like to offer further information or suggestions or provide photographs are invited to write to the author.

The Mould Numbers
THE MOULD NUMBERS BELOW ARE FROM THE SHAW AND COPESTAKE FACTORY AND SHOULD NOT CONTAIN ANY FALCON WARE NUMBERS.

See back page for further reading.

Price Guide

The task of assessing prices is a difficult one and it must be borne in mind that these are bound to vary since so much depends on prevailing market conditions.

The price for each pattern and / or shape may vary considerably depending on colour and condition.

In addition, it should be noted that the following decorations could be more than the values quoted.

MATT DARK BLUE

PINK
HAND PAINTED; CELLULOSE OR GLOSS
SPECIAL DECORATIVE EFFECTS SUCH AS MARBLING OR DRIP GLAZE

As a general rule high glaze animals tend to fetch less than matt finish, except in certain lines.

Acknowledgements

Once again, my thanks go to the many collectors who have shared SylvaC information with me. In particular, I gratefully acknowledge the following: Mick and Derry Collins of The SylvaC Collectors Circle, Susan Verbeek, Nick Rees and Leslie Howe.

Mould No	Description	Size	Price Guide in £'s	Colour	Date Purchased	Price Paid
3001	Salt,pepper,mustard 'Wyka' range	3.73"h	20-25			
3002	Sandwich tray 'Wyka' range	11.5"l	10-15			
3003	Double tray 'Wyka' range	11.5"l	10-15			
3004	Triple tray 'Wyka' range	15"l	15-20			
3005	Toast rack 'Wyka' range	9.5"l	15-20			
3006	Vase 'Wyka' range	12.5"h	20-30			
3007	Watercress dish and stand 'Wyka' range		10-20			
3008	N/I					
3009	Jug 'Wyka' range	8"h	20-25			
3010	Butter dish 'Wyka' range	7.25"l	15-18			
3011	Vase 'Wyka' range	7.5"h	15-25			
3012	Mug 'Wyka' range	4.5"h	5-10			
3013	Bowl 'Wyka' range	3.5"dia	5-10			
3014	Posy 'Oak leaf' range	9.5"l	12-15			
3015	Vase 'Oakleaf' range	8"l	10-15			
3016	N/I					
3017	Posy		5-10			
3018	Posy 'Bracken' range		5-10			
3019	Pig money box	4.5"h	12-25			
3020	Jar		5-8			
3021	N/I					
3022	Plant pot 'Magnolia' range	5.75"h	25-45			
3023	Vase 'Bracken' range	8.25"l	14-18			

Mould No	Description	Size	Price Guide in £'s	Colour	Date Purchased	Price Paid
3024	N/I					
3025	Vase 'Slymcraft' range	6.25"h	5-10			
3026	Vase		5-10			
3027	Vase		5-10			
3028	Vase		5-10			
3029	Vase 'Slymcraft' range	12"h	15-20			
3030	Vase 'Slymcraft' range	7.5"h	8-12			
3031	Vase 'Chesterfield' range	6"h	8-12			
3032	Vase 'Slymcraft' range	8.75"h	10-15			
3033	Vase		5-10			
3034	Vase		5-10			
3035	Vase		5-10			
3036	Vase 'Slymcraft' range	7.75"h	10-15			
3037	Vase 'Slymcraft' range	9.75"h	10-18			
3038	Vase 'Slymcraft' range	9.5"h	10-18			
3039	Vase 'Slymcraft' range		9-12			
3040	Vase 'Slymcraft' range	3.75"h	5-8			
3041	Vase		5-10			
3042	Vase 'Slymcraft' range	7.75"h	10-15			
3043	Vase 'Slymcraft' range	4.75"h	5-8			
3044	Vase 'Slymcraft' range	7.5"h	7-12			
3045	Vase		5-10			
3046	Vase 'Slymcraft' range	7.5"h	8-10			

Mould No	Description	Size	Price Guide in £'s	Colour	Date Purchased	Price Paid
3047	Vase 'Slymcraft' range	9.5"h	10-18			
3048	Vase 'Slymcraft' range	7.75"h	7-10			
3049	Vase 'Slymcraft' range	12"h	15-20			
3050	Vase cylindrical	3"h	5-8			
3051	Vase 'Slymcraft' range	7.5"h	8-12			
3052	Vase 'Slymcraft' range	6.5"h	8-12			
3053	Vase 'Chesterfield' range	10.25"h	18-22			
3054	Vase 'Chesterfield' range	8.25"h	10-18			
3055	Vase 'Slymcraft' range	9.5"h	10-18			
3056	Vase 'Slymcraft' range	9.5"h	10-18			
3057	Plant pot 'Chesterfield' range	5"h	15-20			
3058	Plant pot 'Chesterfield' range	6"h	15-20			
3059	Vase 'Slymcraft' range	7.75"h	8-12			
3060	Vase		8-12			
3061	Vase 'Slymcraft' range	9.75"h	10-18			
3062	Vase 'Slymcraft' range	7.5"h	8-12			
3063	Vase 'Slymcraft' range	5.5"h	5-8			
3064	Vase specimen 'Slymcraft' range	10"h	10-15			
3065	Vase 'Slymcraft' range	3.5"h	5-8			
3066	Vase 'Slymcraft' range	5.5"h	5-8			
3067	Vase 'Slymcraft' range	10"h	10-15			
3068	Bowl 'Slymcraft' range	5.5"dia	5-8			
3069	Vase long	9.5"l	5-10			

Mould No	Description	Size	Price Guide in £'s	Colour	Date Purchased	Price Paid
3070	Vase		5-10			
3071	Bowl 'Slymcraft' range	7.75"dia	8-12			
3072	Vase long	6.5"l	4-8			
3073	Vase		5-10			
3074	Dog		25-30			
3075	Cat Manx	3.5"h	30-45			
3076	Flower holder		10-15			
3077	Dog Dachshund	6.5"h	40-60			
3078	Dog Dachshund	5"h	30-45			
3079	N/I					
3080	Basket		10-15			
3081	Bowl		10-15			
3082	Vase		5-10			
3083	Bowl		10-15			
3084	Vase long low		10-15			
3085	Dish banana shape	10"l	4-10			
3086	Ashtray round used for advertising	6.25"dia	10-15			
3087	N/I					
3088	Zebra		20-35			
3089	Vase		5-12			
3090-3091	N/I					
3092	Spaniel	4"h	20-30			
3093	Toothache dog	4"h	30-40			

Mould No	Description	Size	Price Guide in £'s	Colour	Date Purchased	Price Paid
3094-3095	N/I					
3096	Dog Terrier	4.5"h	20-30			
3097	Rabbit	5.5"h	30-45			
3098	Vase 'Lily' range	6.5"l	30-45			
3099	Candle holder		8-12			
3100	Flower trough 'Chesterfield' range	7.5"l	15-20			
3101	Posy vase 'Lily ' range	10"l	50-70			
3102	Kitten chasing tail		150+			
3103	N/I					
3104	Vase		5-12			
3105	Ashtray		2-5			
3106	Character jug 'Robert Burns'	5.75"h	30-45			
3107	Vase		5-12			
3108-3109	N/I					
3110	Dog Poodle	4.75"h	20-30			
3111	Wall vase		15-25			
3111	Girl 'Pam'	3"h	60-85			
3112	Boy 'Paul'	2.75"h	60-85			
3113	Boy 'Pete'	3.25"h	60-85			
3114	Dog puppy	3"h	18-30			
3115	Duckling	2"h	20-30			
3116	Dog puppy	2.25"h	20-30			
3117	Duckling	2"h	30-45			

Mould No	Description	Size	Price Guide in £'s	Colour	Date Purchased	Price Paid
3118	Dog puppy	3.5"h	25-40			
3119	Horse	5.5"h	20-30			
3120	Hare	4"h	20-30			
3121	Cat scared	2.5"h	40-50			
3122	Ashtray		20-30			
3122	Ash tray with dog or wall clock		30-40			
3123	Mongrel sitting	5.5"h	30-40			
3124	Dog Dachshund	4.5"h	20-35			
3125	Dog Alsatian		30-45			
3126	Dog Dachshund	4"h	30-40			
3127	Dog St Bernard		30-40			
3128	Dog Corgi sitting	4.25"h	30-40			
3129	Horse with riding gear	5.5"h	25-30			
3130	Horse standing	5.5"h	25-30			
3131	Donkey		25-30			
3132	Dog with with baskets	2.25"h	30-40			
3133	Puppy Corgi sitting	2.5"h	15-25			
3134	Puppy Corgi very small	1.5"h	15-25			
3135	Puppy Corgi lying down	2"h	15-25			
3136	Dog Corgi on all fours	4"h	25-35			
3137	Puppy Corgi on all fours	2.75"h	10-20			
3138	Donkey and cart or panniers	4"h	30-40			
3139	Donkey	4"h	25-30			

Mould No	Description	Size	Price Guide in £'s	Colour	Date Purchased	Price Paid
3140	Elephant caricature with big ears	5"l	40-60			
3141	Monkey with boxing gloves	4.75"h	35-50			
3142	Dog		20-30			
3143	Dog		20-30			
3144	Horse with head down	5"h	20-30			
3145	Foal standing	4.25"h	20-30			
3146	Cockerel		30-50			
3147	Donkey with amused expression		40-60			
3148	N/I					
3149	Cart horse		25-35			
3150	Foal on all fours	4"h	20-30			
3151	Cat lying down	5.5"h	35-50			
3152	Horse standing as Zebra	10"h	30-50 40-60			
3153	Tiger lying down	5.5"h	35-50			
3154	Stag lying down	6.5"h	30-50			
3155	Cart horse	6.5"h	20-35			
3156	Swallow wall plaque	6.5"l	30-50			
3157	Swallow wall plaque	5"l	20-40			
3158	Swallow wall plaque	4.5"l	20-30			
3159-3161	N/I					
3162	Grebe on foot to go in bowl	3.5"h	30-50			
3163	cat		20-30			
3164	Dog Pekinese puppy	2.5"h	10-20			

Mould No	Description	Size	Price Guide in £'s	Colour	Date Purchased	Price Paid
3165	Dog Pekinese	3"h	10-25			
3166	Dog Stafford Bull Terrier	4.5"h	20-30			
3167	Cat sitting	5"h	45-50			
3168	Kitten in ball of wool	2.75"h	20-35			
3169	Dog Golden Retriever	5"h	15-25			
3170	Dog Alsation	5.75"h	20-35			
3171	Dog Alsation	4"h	15-25			
3172	Goat	5"h	30-40			
3173	Dog Chow on all fours	4.75"h	20-35			
3174	Dog Poodle frolicking	5.75"h	20-35			
3175	Dog Dachshund on hind legs	5.5"h	25-40			
3176	Horse standing	7.25"h	20-30			
3177	Dog Sealyham puppy	5"h	35-50			
3178	Dog		15-25			
3179	Dog Sealyham	4"h	35-50			
3180	Horse	9"h	30-40			
3180	Horse and trap	17.5"l	45-65			
3181	N/I					
3182	Dog cartoon style Goofy	5.5"h	35-50			
3183	'Toothache dog'	5.25"h	40-50			
3184	N/I					
3185	Bowl		8-10			
3186	Tray		8-12			

Mould No	Description	Size	Price Guide in £'s	Colour	Date Purchased	Price Paid
3187	Dog condiment set salt pepper mustard		50-75			
3188	Bowl 'Chesterfield' range		10-15			
3189	Vase 'Slymcraft' long low	14.5"l	10-15			
3190	Bowl 'Chesterfield' range	9.25"l	10-20			
3191	Bowl		10-15			
3192	Vase		10-20			
3193	Bulb bowl brick pattern	9"l	12-20			
3194	Bulb bowl brick pattern	6.25"l	12-18			
3195	Bowl		10-15			
3196	Bowl 'Magnolia' range	8"dia	45-75			
3197	Basket		10-15			
3198-3202	N/I					
3203	Jug	5.75"h	10-20			
3204	Jug small 'Avon' shape	3.5"h	8-10			
3205	N/I					
3206	Butter dish 'Avon' shape	7"l	15-20			
3207	Cheese dish 'Avon' shape		15-20			
3208	Sandwich Tray 'Avon' shape	12.5"l	10-15			
3209	Honey jar 'Avon' shape	4"h	5-10			
3210	Vase low trellis design	7.5"l	10-15			
3211	Vase		10-15			
3212	Bowl		10-15			
3213	Bowl 'Magnolia' long oval	13.5"l	25-40			

Mould No	Description	Size	Price Guide in £'s	Colour	Date Purchased	Price Paid
3214	Bowl 'Magnolia' range oval	4.25"l	20-30			
3215	Trough 'Magnolia' range	7.5"l	15-25			
3216	Vase 'Magnolia' range	10"h	55-70			
3217	Vase 'Magnolia' range	8"h	30-50			
3218	Bowl 'Magnolia' range round		15-30			
3219	Tankard	5"h	15-20			
3220	Tankard	5"h	15-20			
3221	Vase 'Magnolia' range 2 handled	12"l	45-60			
3222	Bowl		8-12			
3223	Log vase		8-12			
3224	Bowl		8-12			
3225	Vase 'Slymcraft' range 2 handled	14"l	15-25			
3226	Tankard	5"h	15-20			
3227	Bowl		10-15			
3228	Vase		10-15			
3229	N/l					
3230	Vase fish shape	7"h	15-20			
3231	Triple candle holder	13"l	20-28			
3232	Vase		10-15			
3233	Bowl log shape	8"l	15-20			
3234	Bowl log shape	4.5"l	10-15			
3235	Bowl log shape	4"l	8-12			
3236	Vase		10-15			

Mould No	Description	Size	Price Guide in £'s	Colour	Date Purchased	Price Paid
3237	Tray		8-12			
3238	Cup 'Avon' shape	3"h	5-8			
3239	Elephant money box also	4.25"h	25-35			
3239	Elephant with posy on back	4.5"h	25-35			
3240	Pig		20-25			
3241	Dog		20-25			
3242	N/I					
3243	Bowl	8.75"l	15-20			
3244	Bowl	6"l	15-20			
3245	Jar		15-20			
3246	Bowl		15-20			
3247	Vase 'Lily' range	10"h	40-55			
3248	N/I					
3249	Bowl		10-15			
3250	Vase		10-15			
3251	Bowl		10-15			
3252	Vase		10-15			
3253	Cup		2-5			
3254	Bowl		10-15			
3255	Vase 'Chesterfield' range	10"h	15-25			
3256	Vase 'Chesterfield' range	8"h	15-25			
3257	Plate 2 scroll handle	9"dia	10-12			
3258	Jug small		8-10			

Mould No	Description	Size	Price Guide in £'s	Colour	Date Purchased	Price Paid
3259	Bowl		8-10			
3260	Bowl		10-15			
3261	Vase 'Fuchsia' range also		20-28			
3261	Plate	10"dia	8-10			
3262	Bowl 'Fuchsia' boat shape also	14"l	30-40			
3262	Plate # 'Avon' shape	8"dia	5-8			
3263	Vase 'Fuchsia' range		20-25			
3263	Plate # 'Avon' shape	6.5"dia	5-8			
3264	Cereal bowl # 'Avon' shape	6.25"dia	5-8			
3265	Trough 'Fuchsia' range	7.75"l	15-20			
3265	Fruit bowl 'Avon' shape		10-15			
3266	Vase 'Fuchsia' range	6.75"l	15-20			
3266	Cake plate 'Avon' shape	10.5"dia	8-10			
3267	Cake stand single tier 'Avon' shape	8"dia	15-20			
3268	Cake stand 2 tier 'Avon' shape		20-25			
3268	Vase 'Fuchsia' range	9"h	25-30			
3269	Vase 'Fuchsia' range	7.75"h	20-25			
3269	Fruit bowl 'Avon' shape	8.5"dia	12-18			
3270	Plant pot 'Fuchsia' range	5"h	15-20			
3270	Soup bowl 'Avon' shape		8-8			
3271	Plant pot 'Fuchsia' range		15-20			
3272	Vase 'Fuchsia' range	12"l	20-25			
3273	Tankard embossed fox mask	3.75"h	12-20			

Mould No	Description	Size	Price Guide in £'s	Colour	Date Purchased	Price Paid
3274	Tankard embossed hound head	3.75"h	12-20			
3274	Tankard also 1972 Stoke City cup final	3.75"h	20-40			
3275	Dog Spaniel with pipe	5.25"h	35-55			
3276	Dog Spaniel with ball	3.25"h	35-55			
3277	Vase		10-15			
3278	Tankard embossed horse head	3.75"h	12-20			
3279	Character jug George Bernard Shaw	5.5"h	30-45			
3280	Bowl log shape	6"l	8-12			
3281	Cup		3-5			
3282	Flower jug	15"h	30-50			
3283	Vase 'Lily' range	8.25"h	35-45			
3284	Vase		5-10			
3285	Vase 'Lily' range large		45-55			
3286	Vase 'Lily' range	12"h	50-60			
3287	Bowl 'Lily' range oval	9.5"l	30-45			
3288	Plant pot 'Lily' range	8"dia	45-55			
3289	Posy 'Lily' range	7.25"l	25-35			
3290	Vase 'Lily' range	11.5"h	50-60			
3291	Plant pot 'Lily' range	7"dia	30-45			
3292	Bowl 'Lily' range		25-35			
3293-3295	N/I					
3296	Condiment set 'Avon' shape 4 piece		15-20			
3297	Cheese board +knife 'Avon' shape	9.75"l	15-20			

Mould No	Description	Size	Price Guide in £'s	Colour	Date Purchased	Price Paid
3298	Vase		5-10			
3299	Toast rack 'Avon' shape	7.5"l	15-20			
3300-3302	N/l					
3303	Vase		10-15			
3304	Beaker		8-12			
3305	Vase		10-15			
3306	Tankard		10-15			
3307	Cat		20-25			
3308	Vase		10-15			
3309	Vase		10-15			
3310	Vase 'Slymcraft' oval		10-15			
3311	Bowl with bird		25-35			
3312	Vase	6.5"h	10-18			
3313	Cupid flower holder	3.75"h	15-20			
3314	Dog Fox Terrier	5.75"h	25-40			
3315	Coffee pot 'Avon' shape 2 pint	9"h	10-20			
3316	Vase	8.5"h	10-20			
3317	Dog standing Wire Haired Fox Terrier	5.5"h	25-40			
3318	Dog lying asleep Wire Haired Fox Terrier	5"l	25-40			
3319	Puppy dog sitting		20-30			
3320	Puppy dog Dachshund sitting	4.5"l	20-30			
3321	Dog Alsatian sitting	6"h	20-35			
3322	Lop eared rabbit medium		25-40			

Mould No	Description	Size	Price Guide in £'s	Colour	Date Purchased	Price Paid
3323	Vase	6.25"h	12-18			
3324	Vase	10"h	18-20			
3325	Cupid flower holder round	4.5"h	8-15			
3326	Lop eared rabbit large		35-50			
3327	Rabbit ears up		25-40			
3328	Rabbit ears up	8"h	35-50			
3329	Vase Shell range	7"h	15-20			
3330	Vase	8"h	12-18			
3331	Plant pot ribbed		12-18			
3332	Plant pot square		12-18			
3333	Cupid flower holder	4.5"h	8-12			
3334	Vase sea shell	5"l	8-12			
3335	Dog Spaniel sitting		15-25			
3336	Flower pot square ribbed		8-12			
3337	Pig	2.5"h	10-15			
3338	Dog sitting Highland Terrier		25-30			
3339	Bird Osprey 'Prestige piece'	8.5"h	55-90			
3340	Ginger jar and cover	6"h	10-15			
3341	Vase 'Opelle' range oval		10-15			
3342	Vase	7"h	10-18			
3343	Vase	5.5"h	8-12			
3344	Vase	5"h	8-12			
3345	Vase long low		8-12			

Mould No	Description	Size	Price Guide in £'s	Colour	Date Purchased	Price Paid
3346	Pig's head money box		20-35			
3347	Vase fluted	7.5"h	15-20			
3348	Vase	10.5"l	15-20			
3349	Vase 'Pebbles' range	10"l	18-25			
3350	Vase 'Pebbles' range	6.75"h	12-18			
3351	Plant pot 'Alpine' range		15-20			
3352	Ginger jar embossed		10-15			
3353	Coffee pot 'Avon' small		18-25			
3354	Covered jar square		8-12			
3355	Bowl 'Pebbles' range	6.75"dia	15-20			
3356	Bowl oblong with figure		25-30			
3357	Jar 'Blossom' range		8-12			
3358	Vase 'Pebbles' range	9"h	15-22			
3359	Jar square etched		8-12			
3360	Posy vase 'Pebble' range	11.5"l	15-20			
3361	Plant pot 'Pebble' range	4.5"h	10-18			
3362	Vase flat sides	5"h	8-12			
3363	Posy vase	8.5"l	5-10			
3364	Vase 'Alpine' range	8"h	10-20			
3365	Posy vase	6.5"l	5-10			
3366	Posy vase	4"l	4-8			
3367	Square jar etched pattern		8-12			
3368	Vase 'Pebbles' range	11.25"h	18-25			

Mould No	Description	Size	Price Guide in £'s	Colour	Date Purchased	Price Paid
3369	Vase rope handles 'Alpine' range	8"h	10-20			
3370	Sea Horse with shell bowl	10"h	30-40			
3371	Vase rope handles 'Alpine' range	11"h	15-25			
3372	Tea caddy elephant head handles 'Rington's'	7.5"h	12-18			
3373	Vase	3.25"h	5-8			
3374	Vase etched pattern	5.5"h	8-12			
3375	Vase embossed pattern	5.5"h	8-12			
3376	Vase	5.5"h	5-8			
3377	Plant pot	5"h	12-18			
3378	Tray 'Feather' range	7.5"l	10-15			
3379	Vase rope handles 'Alpine' range	8"h	10-20			
3380	Vase rope handle 'Alpine' range	8"h	10-20			
3381	Vase 'Alpine' range	11"h	18-22			
3382	Vase 'Alpine' range	6"h	5-10			
3383	Mule comical sitting	6.5"h	25-40			
3384	Mule comical standing	6.5"h	25-40			
3385	Vase rope sides 'Alpine' range	8"h	10-20			
3386	Vase rope sides 'Alpine' range		10-20			
3387	Bowl rope sides 'Alpine' range	Small	10-15			
3388	Bowl rope sides 'Alpine' range	Large	12-20			
3389	Pot rope sides 'Alpine' range		15-25			
3390	Pot rope sides 'Alpine' range		12-18			
3391	Posy bar rope sides 'Alpine' range		5-10			

Mould No	Description	Size	Price Guide in £'s	Colour	Date Purchased	Price Paid
3392	Cat long neck embossed with flowers	12.75"h	50-85			
3393	Duck	4.5"h	45-60			
3394	Ashtray for pipe textured	4.74"l	5-10			
3395	Pot small 'Alpine' range for ferns		12-18			
3396	Pot large 'Alpine' range for ferns		15-25			
3397	Flower Jug 'Alpine' range	10"h	20-30			
3398	Vase 'Alpine' range	9"h	12-20			
3399	Vase 'Alpine' range	8"h	10-18			
3400	Vase 'Alpine' range	6"h	5-10			
3401	Bowl large 'Alpine' range oval		10-20			
3403	Cat Long neck	7"h	25-30			
3404	Cat Siamese caricature	6.5"h	15-25			
3405	Jar	6"h	5-10			
3406	Cat caricature back paw scratching	4.75"h	45-60			
3407	Cat caricature front paw in ear.	4.5"h	45-60			
3408	Beaker		5-10			
3409	Ashtray	4.75"l	2-5			
3410	Ashtray as box		5-12			
3411	Mug		8-12			
3412	Vase		5-10			
3413	Beaker ears of wheat		8-12			
3414	Sea Horse vase	8"h	18-25			
3415	Plant pot 'Pebbles' range	6"h	20-25			

Mould No	Description	Size	Price Guide in £'s	Colour	Date Purchased	Price Paid
3416	Vase		5-10			
3417	Covered jar		8-12			
3418	Puppy dog Shetland Sheepdog		25-30			
3419	Bowl 'Pebbles' range	6.5"l	8-12			
3420	Posy vase 'Pebbles' range	7.5"l	8-12			
3421	Honey pot		8-12			
3422	Dog Spaniel 'Big Ead' range	3.75"h	40-50			
3423	Dog English sheepdog 'Big Ead' range	3"h	40-50			
3424	Dog Pekinese 'Big Ead' range	2.75"h	30-40			
3425	Dog Alsatian 'Big Ead' range	3.5"h	30-40			
3426	Dog Dachshund 'Big Ead' range	3"h	30-40			
3427	Dog St Bernard 'Big Ead' range	3"h	30-40			
3428	Dog Poodle 'Big Ead' range	3.5"h	30-40			
3429	Dog Bulldog 'Big Ead' range	3"h	30-40			
3430	Dog Shetland Sheepdog 'Funnies' range	3.5"h	30-40			
3431	Dog Scottie 'Big Ead' range	3.25"h	30-40			
3432	Dog Yorkshire Terrier 'Funnies' range	3"h	30-40			
3433	Dog with mouth open 'Big Ead' range	4.25"h	30-40			
3434	Vase long low 'Pebbles' range	13.5"l	15-20			
3435	Ash box horses		15-20			
3436	Ashbox fish		15-20			
3437	Ashbox duck		15-20			
3438	Plinth		2-3			

Mould No	Description	Size	Price Guide in £'s	Colour	Date Purchased	Price Paid
3439	Bowl 'Pebbles' range	9.75"l	10-18			
3440	Bowl 'Pebbles' range	6.5"l	8-15			
3441	Vase	6"h	5-12			
3442	Beaker		5-8			
3443	Vase oval 'Chequers' range	8"h	10-20			
3444	Vase 'Chequers' range		8-15			
3445	Sea horse with shell bowl small		20-28			
3446	Basket		8-12			
3447	Dog Cairn Terrier	5"h	15-25			
3448	Vase		5-10			
3449	Vase 'Opelle' range	6"h	5-10			
3450	Vase 'Opelle' range	8"h	10-20			
3451	Vase 'Opelle' range	10"h	18-22			
3452	Tea cup embossed		3-5			
3453	Posy 'Opelle' range		5-10			
3454	Hors d'oeuvre tray with six dishes		15-20			
3455	Plant pot 'Opelle' range large		15-25			
3456	Plant pot 'Opelle' range small		10-15			
3457	Cat Siamese caricature	13"h	40-55			
3458	Vase 'Opelle' range		5-10			
3459	Otter with fish 'Prestige' range	9.5"l	120-140			
3460	Vase 'Sea Horse' range	10"h	30-40			
3461	Bowl oblong 'Opelle' range large	5"h	10-25			

Mould No	Description	Size	Price Guide in £'s	Colour	Date Purchased	Price Paid
3462	Bowl oblong 'Opelle' range small		8-18			
3463	Bowl square		10-15			
3464	Planter	15"l	5-10			
3465	Flower bowl 'Opelle' range	9.5"sq	10-20			
3466	Wall vase 'Opelle' range		15-22			
3467	Ashtray		2-5			
3468	Cup fluted		3-5			
3469	N/l					
3470	Posy 'Sea Horse' range	8"l	12-18			
3471	Posy 'Sea Horse' range	8.5"l	12-18			
3472	Vase 'Sea Horse' range	6"h	10-15			
3473	Vase 'Sea Horse' range small		18-22			
3474	Bowl 'Sea Horse' range large		18-22			
3475	Bowl 'Sea Horse' range small	5"h	15-20			
3476	Plant pot 'Sea Horse' range		20-25			
3477	Vase 'Tudor' range small		5-8			
3478	Shaving mug	4.25"h	10-15			
3479	Bowl		8-12			
3480	Plant pot 'Pebbles' range	5.25"h	15-20			
3481	Ashtray/dish 'Pebbles' range	5.5"l	5-10			
3482	Dish 'Pebbles' range on feet	12.5"l	15-25			
3483	Vase	5"h	8-12			
3484	Celery tray 'Feather' range	13.5"l	20-25			

Mould No	Description	Size	Price Guide in £'s	Colour	Date Purchased	Price Paid
3485	Salad bowl 'Feather' range	12"dia	20-25			
3486	Desert bowl	3.5"h	5-8			
3487	Vase panel front	10"h	18-22			
3488	Tankard plain	3.75"h	8-10			
3488	Tankard Nottingham Forest FC	3.75"h	20-40			
3489	Powder bowl and cover shaped		10-15			
3490	Vase 'Tudor' range	6"h	8-12			
3491	Vase 'Tudor' range	8"h	10-20			
3492	Vase 'Tudor' range	10"h	18-22			
3493	Vase 'Tudor' range large		18-22			
3494	Vase 'Tudor' range small		5-8			
3495	Bowl 'Tudor' range		8-12			
3496	Pot 'Tudor' range large		12-20			
3497	Pot 'Tudor' range small		10-15			
3498	Vase posy 'Tudor' range large		5-10			
3499	Vase posy 'Tudor' range small		5-8			
3500	Dog Labrador	5"h	20-30			
3501	Vase	9"h	12-20			
3502	Twin tray 'Feather' range	10"l	20-25			
3503	Triple tray 'Feather' range	12"l	20-25			
3504	Dish 'Feather' range	12"l	20-25			
3505	Condiment set & tray 'Feather'range	8.75"l	25-30			
3506	Twin tray 'Feather' range	11"l	20-25			

Mould No	Description	Size	Price Guide in £'s	Colour	Date Purchased	Price Paid
3507	Cress dish & stand 'Feather' range	10"dia	20-25			
3508	Cheese dish 'Feather' range		25-30			
3509	Biscuit jar 'Feather' range		20-25			
3510	Quadruple tray 'Feather' range	14.5"l	25-30			
3511	Lidded butter dish 'Feather' range	6.5"l	25-30			
3512	Double dish 'Feather' range	11"l	25-30			
3513	Beaker 'Feather' range		15-20			
3514	Jam/honey pot 'Feather' range		15-20			
3515	Dish 'Feather' range	5.5"l	10-15			
3516	Tea cup		3-5			
3517	Vase panel front large		12-20			
3518	Vase panel front small		5-10			
3519	Cup		3-5			
3520	Butter dish		12-18			
3521	Vase posy		5-8			
3522	Dog Spaniel		25-35			
3523	Vase 'New Shell' range	8"h	10-18			
3524	Vase conch 'New Shell' range	10"h	25-30			
3525	Vase wide 'New Shell' range large		10-20			
3526	Vase 'New Shell' range	5.75"h	10-15			
3527	Wall vase 'New Shell' range		20-30			
3528	Posy 'New Shell' range	11"l	10-15			
3529	Vase 'New Shell' range	7.5"l	12-18			

Mould No	Description	Size	Price Guide in £'s	Colour	Date Purchased	Price Paid
3530	Bowl 'New Shell' range small		8-12			
3531	Bowl 'New Shell' range large		20-25			
3532	Posy 'New Shell' range	7.5"l	8-10			
3533	Bowl on foot small		5-10			
3534	Bowl on foot large		10-15			
3535	Vase		5-10			
3536	Posy vase		5-10			
3537	Bowl fluted		8-12			
3538	Vase	6"h	8-12			
3539	Vase 'Tudor' range	6"h	8-12			
3540	Vase 'Slymcraft' range	8"h	10-20			
3541	Vase 'Tudor' range	8"h	10-20			
3542	Mr SylvaC Advertising model	8"h	120-150			
3543	Cup		3-5			
3544	Cup		3-5			
3545	Bowl		5-8			
3546	Beer mug	3.5"h	8-12			
3547	Cup and saucer 'Magnolia' range		5-10			
3548	Vase on foot	8"h	12-18			
3549	Vase on foot	8.25"h	12-18			
3550	Lamp base	15.5"h	30-35			
3551	Vase		5-10			
3552	Dog Pug	4.5"h	25-35			

Mould No	Description	Size	Price Guide in £'s	Colour	Date Purchased	Price Paid
3553	Urn 'Vintage' range	7"h	12-18			
3554	Butter dish butterfly handle		20-25			
3555	Bowl	4"dia	8-12			
3556	Posy log vase		5-8			
3556	Posy log vase with animal		25-30			
3557	Vase 'Lily' range	8"h	20-30			
3558	Vase	13"h	15-25			
3559	Urn 'Vintage' range	5"h	10-15			
3560	Vase dog jumping wall	3.25"h	15-25			
3561	Dog Basset Hound sitting	6.75"h	25-35			
3562	Bowl 'New Shell' range	12"dia	10-20			
3563	Dog Basset Hound sitting	5.75"h	25-35			
3564	Tea cup butterfly on handle	3"h	3-7			
3565	Dog Scottie small	2.5"h	20-30			
3566	Barrel box		10-15			
3567	Dog Spaniel small	2.5"h	20-30			
3568	Giraffe	10"h	25-35			
3569	Jug 'Avon' shape 1 pint	5.5"h	10-20			
3570	Elephant sitting		25-35			
3571	Basket and kitten		20-25			
3572	Vase two handles		8-12			
3573	Bowl	5"dia	8-12			
3574	Not used					

Mould No	Description	Size	Price Guide in £'s	Colour	Date Purchased	Price Paid
3575	Hare	7"h	30-45			
3576	Honey pot with butterfly	4.5"h	15-20			
3577	Vase		5-10			
3578	Urn 'Vintage' range	9.5"h	15-20			
3579	Urn 'Vintage' range	11"h	15-25			
3580	N/I					
3581	Vegetable dish		12-20			
3582	Soup bowl		5-8			
3583	Penguin		20-30			
3584	Flower Jug on foot	11"h	20-30			
3585	Bird Toucan		20-30			
3586	Dog lying down		20-30			
3587	Vase on feet	8"h	12-18			
3589	Cheese board with dish		12-20			
3590	Pot woven pattern	4"h	10-15			
3591	Vase on feet	6"h	8-12			
3592	Bowl on foot	11"dia	12-22			
3593	N/I					
3594	Meat dish oval	15.5"l	15-25			
3595	Vase	8"h	10-20			
3596	Jug 'Feather' range		18-25			
3597	Pot woven pattern		10-15			
3598	Vase oval		5-10			

Mould No	Description	Size	Price Guide in £'s	Colour	Date Purchased	Price Paid
3599	Sugar bowl 'Feather' range		10-15			
3600	Jug 'Feather' range small		15-25			
3601	Jug 'Feather' range large		20-30			
3602	Vase embossed		5-10			
3603	Vase embossed		5-10			
3604	Jug butterfly handle		8-10			
3605	Pot		5-8			
3606	Cream jug butterfly handle		8-10			
3607	Sugar bowl butterfly handle		8-10			
3608	Bowl fluted	6"dia	8-12			
3609	Coffee can		3-5			
3610	Cat		20-35			
3611	Gravy boat and stand		12-18			
3612	Mouse	4"h	20-35			
3613	Honey pot bee hive	4.5"h	10-12			
3614	Dog sitting	5"h	25-35			
3615	Dog	5"h	25-35			
3616	Pot embossed		10-15			
3617	Baby mug two handled #	3.5"h	20-30			
3618	Vase	11"l	18-22			
3619	Condiment set on stand butterfly		25-30			
3620	Tea pot butterfly handle		20-35			
3621	Ashtray	6"l	2-5			

Mould No	Description	Size	Price Guide in £'s	Colour	Date Purchased	Price Paid
3622	Jar three cornered		5-10			
3623	Pot embossed		5-10			
3624	Bowl 'Privet' range	7"dia	8-15			
3625	Bowl stone wall effect		8-12			
3626	Top hat	4"h	10-15			
3627	Jar		5-10			
3628	Coffee pot		15-25			
3629	Jar three cornered		5-10			
3630	Coffee pot		15-25			
3631	Vase		5-10			
3632	Beer tankard	5"h	10-12			
3633	Meat dish	12"l	12-20			
3634	Mug		8-12			
3635	Sugar bowl		5-10			
3636	Tray	14.5"l	8-12			
3637	Jar embossed	6"h	5-10			
3638	Bowl stone wall effect	9.5"dia	10-20			
3639	Vase two handles	12.5"h	15-25			
3640	Coffee pot embossed		15-25			
3641	Ashtray		3-6			
3642	Dog Basset hound		20-35			
3643	Vase stone wall effect	9"h	12-20			
3644	Bowl large		15-25			

Mould No	Description	Size	Price Guide in £'s	Colour	Date Purchased	Price Paid
3645	Tray		8-12			
3646	Mug embossed		8-12			
3647	Coffee pot 'Web' pattern		15-25			
3648	Sugar bowl small		5-8			
3649	Sugar bowl large		5-10			
3650	Mug 'Web' pattern		8-12			
3651	Vase	13"h	15-25			
3652	Vase small		8-12			
3653	Vase stone wall effect		10-15			
3654	Vase	11"h	18-22			
3655	Vase on foot	10"h	18-22			
3656	Vase	8"h	12-20			
3657	Vase	6"h	5-12			
3658	Pot small		10-15			
3659	Pot large		15-20			
3660	Ashtray on three feet		8-10			
3661	Beer mug one pint	5.5"h	8-12			
3662	Vase	6"h	5-10			
3663	Bowl on foot small		8-12			
3664	Mug on foot		8-12			
3665	Bowl on foot medium		10-15			
3666	Bowl on foot large		10-20			
3667	Sugar bowl on foot	2.5"h	5-8			

Mould No	Description	Size	Price Guide in £'s	Colour	Date Purchased	Price Paid
3668	Tea pot on foot		20-30			
3669	Cream jug on foot	3.5"h	5-8			
3670	Coffee pot		15-25			
3671	Tea cup on foot		3-5			
3672	Tea cup embossed on foot		3-5			
3673	Butter dish round on foot		15-20			
3674	Ashtray tyre	5.5"dia	5-10			
3675	Grandfather clock	2"h	20-25			
3675	Dog		25-35			
3676	Jar	6"h	5-10			
3677	Cheese dish square on foot		15-20			
3678	Vase 'Palm Leaf' range	8"h	12-18			
3679	Butter dish oblong butterfly handle		15-20			
3680	Pot 'New shell' range		12-18			
3681	Bowl fluted		10-15			
3682	Ashtray	4"l	3-8			
3683	Lamp base 'Pebble' range	12"h	30-40			
3684	Posy vase shell shape	6.5"h	5-10			
3685	Honey pot on foot	4.5"h	8-10			
3686	Butter dish oblong on foot		12-18			
3687	Coffee pot on foot large		20-30			
3688	Beaker		8-10			
3689	Vase		5-10			

Mould No	Description	Size	Price Guide in £'s	Colour	Date Purchased	Price Paid
3690	Vase 'Palm Leaf' range	8"h	12-18			
3691	Covered bowl	4"h	8-12			
3692	Vase 'Chequers' range large		18-22			
3693	Vase 'Chequers' range medium		10-15			
3694	Vase 'Chequers' range	8"h	10-15			
3695	Vase 'Chequers' range small		8-12			
3696	Bowl on foot 'Chequers' range	5.75"l	8-12			
3697	Bowl	10"dia	10-20			
3698	Bowl 'Chequers' range	6.75"l	10-15			
3699	Plant pot 'Chequers' range large		15-25			
3700	Plant pot 'Chequers' range medium		15-25			
3701	Plant pot 'Chequers' range small		12-18			
3702	Posy bar		5-10			
3703	Posy		5-10			
3704	Vase	4.5"h	5-8			
3705	Vase 'Chequers' range	6.5"h	8-12			
3706	Menu holder	6"h	15-20			
3707	Posy on foot		5-10			
3708	Butter dish		12-20			
3709	Card holder	3"l	10-15			
3710	Bowl 'Palm leaf' range	4.5"h	10-15			
3711	Irish harp	4.5"h	8-12			
3712	Ashtray square		2-5			

Mould No	Description	Size	Price Guide in £'s	Colour	Date Purchased	Price Paid
3713	Condiment set and tray	8.5"l	15-20			
3714	Vase 'Palm Leaf' range	6.75"h	15-20			
3715	Plant pot 'Palm Leaf' range	6"h	15-20			
3716	Bowl 'Palm Leaf' range oval		15-20			
3717	Slipper vase 'Palm Leaf' range		8-12			
3718	Bowl boat shape 'Palm Leaf' range large		15-20			
3719	Bowl boat shape 'Palm Leaf' range small		15-20			
3720	Vase 'Palm Leaf' range low	8.5"l	10-15			
3721	Wall vase 'Palm Leaf' range		20-25			
3722	Plant pot 'Palm Leaf' range	4.75"h	15-18			
3723	Vase 'Palm Leaf' range		8-12			
3724	Vase 'Palm Leaf' range	10"h	20-30			
3725	Vase 'Palm Leaf' range	6"h	15-20			
3726	Bowl oval 'Palm Leaf' range		10-15			
3727	Jug on foot 1 pint		10-20			
3728	Cream jug		8-10			
3729	Cream jug 'Web' pattern		8-10			
3730	Ashtray		2-5			
3731	Vase 'Oslo' range	9.5"h	12-18			
3732	Vase 'Oslo' range	8"h	12-18			
3733	Vase 'Oslo' range	6"h	5-10			
3734	Bowl 'Oslo' range large		10-12			
3735	Bowl 'Oslo' range medium		8-15			

Mould No	Description	Size	Price Guide in £'s	Colour	Date Purchased	Price Paid
3736	Bowl 'Oslo' range small		5-10			
3737	Plant pot 'Oslo' range	4.5"h	10-15			
3738	Plant pot 'Oslo' range	6.5"h	12-20			
3739	Posy vase 'Oslo' range		5-10			
3740	Vase 'Oslo' range	6.25"l	8-12			
3741	Vase 'Oslo' range	9.25"l	10-15			
3742	Mug baby size #	3.25"h	5-8			
3743	Bowl 'Oslo' range	3.75"dia	8-12			
3744	Bread and butter plate with butterfly		10-15			
3745	Sandwich plate with butterfly	12.5"l	10-15			
3746	Tea pot with butterfly		20-35			
3747	Mug half pint 'Tudor' range		8-10			
3748	Mug half pint		8-10			
3749	Mug half pint embossed		8-10			
3750	Mug as pineapple		10-12			
3751	Mug		8-10			
3752	Vase	10"h	18-22			
3753	Jar		5-10			
3754	Money box cat's head		20-35			
3755	Bird	4"h	20-30			
3756	Pie funnel bird's head	2"h	10-15			
3757	Tea cup on foot		3-5			
3758	Jar		5-10			

Mould No	Description	Size	Price Guide in £'s	Colour	Date Purchased	Price Paid
3759	Plate flutted	10"dia	5-10			
3760	Ashtray bowl		2-5			
3761	Tray	15"l	5-10			
3762	Horse		25-35			
3763	Money box lifeboat man's head		25-35			
3764	Jar square		5-10			
3765	Dog Scottie sitting		25-35			
3766	Dog Poodle sitting	6"h	25-35			
3767	Dog Corgi sitting	6"h	25-35			
3768	Triple tray		10-15			
3769	Vase	10.5"l	18-22			
3770	Money box cat's head		25-35			
3771	Cheese dish oblong New 'Wishing well' range		15-20			
3772	Honey pot New 'Wishing well' range		10-15			
3773	Butter dish New 'Wishing well' range		15-20			
3774-3787	Not used					
3788	Egg cup nursery ware #		10-15			
3789	Stork	9"h	30-45			
3790	Stork	6"h	25-35			
3791	Baby plate nursery ware #	6"dia	15-20			
3792	Vase		5-10			
3793	Vase square		5-10			
3794	Vase round large		15-18			

Mould No	Description	Size	Price Guide in £'s	Colour	Date Purchased	Price Paid
3795	Vase round small		8-12			
3796	Vase		8-12			
3797	Vase		8-12			
3798	Dog Spaniel siting		25-35			
3799	Character jug lifeboat man		25-35			
3800	Vase square		5-10			
3801	Vase round		5-10			
3802	Money box Seaman Jones small		25-35			
3803	Lamp base 'Tudor' range	10"h	30-35			
3804	Lamp base	9.75"h	25-30			
3805	Lamp		25-30			
3806	Bowl oblong	10.5"l	10-20			
3807	Plant pot stone wall effect	5.5"h	15-20			
3808	Plant pot stone wall effect	4.75"h	12-18			
3809	Plant pot stone wall effect.	4.5"h	12-18			
3810	Vase stone wall effect	10"h	15-20			
3811	Vase stone wall effect	8"h	12-18			
3812	Vase stone wall effect	6"h	8-12			
3813	Bowl stone wall effect		8-12			
3814	Twin vase stone wall effect	13"h	15-25			
3815	Bowl stone wall effect	12"l	10-20			
3816	Vase stone wall effect		5-10			
3817	Bowl/Vase stone wall effect	14"h	15-25			

Mould No	Description	Size	Price Guide in £'s	Colour	Date Purchased	Price Paid
3818	Tray stone wall effect	7"l	8-12			
3819	Posy vase stone wall effect	14"l	5-10			
3820	Posy vase stone wall effect small		3-8			
3821	Bowl 'Glost' range	7.5"l	10-15			
3822	Bowl 'Glost' range oval	11"l	10-12			
3823	Bowl 'Glost' range large		10-20			
3824	Vase 'Privet' range	5"h	15-20			
3825	Vase 'Privet' range	7"h	12-15			
3826	Bowl stone wall effect		8-12			
3827	Dog slipper in mouth	5"h	30-40			
3828	Coffee pot 'Avon' shape	8.25"h	15-25			
3829	Dog Scottie		25-35			
3830	Slipper stone wall effect		8-15			
3831	Tray stone wall effect	13"l	8-12			
3832	Jug		10-15			
3833	Jar		5-10			
3834	Jug 'Wisdom & Providence '	8.5"h	15-20			
3835	Bowl		10-15			
3836	Coffee pot		12-20			
3837	Money box teddy bear policeman		25-35			
3838	Bowl 'Manhattan' range		10-15			
3839	Money box bunnies bank		25-35			
3840	Money box cowboy		25-35			

Mould No	Description	Size	Price Guide in £'s	Colour	Date Purchased	Price Paid
3841	Money box Indian		25-35			
3842	Vase 'Privet' range	8.5"h	12-18			
3843	Bowl and fish		10-20			
3844	Vase 'Privet' range	10.25"h	18-22			
3845	Vase 'Privet' range	6"h	5-10			
3846	Bowl 'Privet' range oval	10"l	15-20			
3847	Cat laughing	6"h	35-45			
3848	Dog Scottie	4"h	25-35			
3849	Fish on base		15-20			
3850	Vase 'Linton' range	4"h	5-8			
3851	Vase 'Linton' range	6"h	5-10			
3852	Vase 'Linton' range	8"h	10-18			
3853	Vase 'Linton' range		12-18			
3854	Posy 'Linton' range		5-8			
3855	Plant pot oval	12"l	15-20			
3856	Vase 'Linton' range		10-15			
3857	Vase 'Linton' range large		15-18			
3858	Pot 'Linton' range large		15-18			
3859	Pot 'Linton' range small		10-15			
3860	Bowl 'Linton' range small		10-15			
3861	Bowl 'Linton' range large		12-20			
3862	Posy slipper 'Linton' range		5-8			
3863	Vase 'Begonia' range	4"h	5-8			

Mould No	Description	Size	Price Guide in £'s	Colour	Date Purchased	Price Paid
3864	Vase 'Begonia' range	6"h	8-12			
3865	Vase 'Begonia' range	8"h	10-15			
3866	Vase 'Begonia' range	10"h	15-20			
3867	Posy 'Begonia' range	7"l	8-12			
3868	Plant pot 'Begonia' range		12-18			
3869	Vase 'Begonia' range	4.5"h	5-8			
3870	Vase 'Begonia' range large		12-18			
3871	Pot 'Begonia' range		12-18			
3872	Pot 'Begonia' range large		15-20			
3873	Bowl 'Begonia' range		8-12			
3874	Bowl 'Begonia' range large		10-20			
3875	Slipper 'Begonia' range		5-8			
3876	Tray 'Begonia' range		3-8			
3877	Vase textured	4"h	5-8			
3878	Vase textured	6"h	5-12			
3879	Vase textured	8"h	10-15			
3880	Vase textured	10"h	15-20			
3881	Posy textured		5-8			
3882	Plant pot textured		12-18			
3883	Vase textured small		4-10			
3884	Vase textured large		12-18			
3885	Pot textured small		5-10			
3886	Pot textured		5-10			

Mould No	Description	Size	Price Guide in £'s	Colour	Date Purchased	Price Paid
3887	Bowl textured	6.75"l	8-12			
3888	Bowl textured		10-20			
3889	Bowl textured		5-8			
3890	Tray textured		5-8			
3891	Not used					
3892	Cat smiling		35-45			
3893	Tray 'Coral' range		8-10			
3894	Bowl 'Privet' range		8-12			
3895	Plant pot 'Privet' range small		12-18			
3896	Plant pot 'Privet' range large		15-20			
3897	Vase 'Coral' range	6"h	15-20			
3898	Vase 'Coral' range		20-25			
3899	Posy ring 'Privet' range		5-8			
3900	Posy bar 'Privet' range		5-8			
3901	Vase 'Coral' range	8"h	20-25			
3902	Posy 'Coral' range		8-10			
3903	Vase 'Privet' range oval	10.5"w	15-20			
3904	Vase 'Coral' range	10"h	25-30			
3905	Vase 'Coral' range oval		15-20			
3906	Pot 'Coral' range		15-20			
3907	Vase 'Coral' range	15.5"w	25-35			
3908	Sugar bowl 'Avon' shape		5-8			
3909	Cream jug 'Avon' shape		5-8			

Mould No	Description	Size	Price Guide in £'s	Colour	Date Purchased	Price Paid
3910	Pot 'Coral' range		18-22			
3911	Dish		5-10			
3912	Squirrel		20-30			
3913	Dog Jack Russell	3.5"h	18-25			
3914	Egg cup 'Avon' shape	1.5"	3-6			
3915	Bread and butter plate 'Lisbon' range		5-10			
3916	Vase		5-10			
3917	Vase		5-10			
3918	Fox		25-35			
3919	Mug half pint embossed	3.75"h	8-12			
3920	Mug half pint		8-12			
3921	Dog	4"h	45-65			
3922	Mug half pint		8-12			
3923	Dog	2"h	40-55			
3924	Vase on foot	10"h	15-20			
3925	'Bambi' fawn		25-35			
3926	Mug		8-12			
3927	Fox caricature	7"h	45-60			
3928	Lamp base		20-30			
3929	Vase tree with rabbits		20-25			
3930	Bull 'Prestige Range'	14.5"l	100-125			
3931	Jar	"h	5-10			
3932	Vase on foot	12"h	15-25			

Mould No	Description	Size	Price Guide in £'s	Colour	Date Purchased	Price Paid
3933	Dog Pomeranian	4.5"h	30-45			
3934	Pot 'Cactus' range	3"h	10-15			
3935	Money box Squirrel	5.75"h	25-35			
3936	Pot 'Cactus'	3"h	10-15			
3937	Tankard 'Wisdom and Providence'	5"h	8-12			
3938	Vase 'Manhattan' range	6.25	5-10			
3939	Vase 'Manhattan' range	8"h	10-15			
3940	Bowl 'Manhattan' range	6.25h	10-15			
3941	Plant pot 'Manhattan' range	6.25"dia	15-20			
3942	Plant pot 'Manhattan' range	5.75" d	15-20			
3943	Plant pot 'Manhattan' range	5"dia	10-15			
3944	Vase 'Manhattan' range	7"l	5-10			
3945	Posy 'Manhattan' range		3-5			
3946	Vase 'Manhattan' range	8"h	10-15			
3947	Vase 'Manhattan' range	10.5"h	12-18			
3948	Tray 'Manhattan' range	12.5"l	10-15			
3949	Bowl 'Manhattan' range large		10-20			
3950	Tray 'Manhattan' range	6.5"l	5-8			
3951	Posy 'Manhattan' range	5"l	5-10			
3952	Posy 'Manhattan' large		5-10			
3953	Ashtray Maple leaf Canada design	5.5"dia	8-12			
3954	Tankard 'Maple leaf' design		8-10			
3955	Tray 'Maple leaf' design		5-10			

Mould No	Description	Size	Price Guide in £'s	Colour	Date Purchased	Price Paid
3956	Vase 'Manhattan' range	11.5"l	8-12			
3957	Fox		20-30			
3958	Lamp base 'Hyacinth' range		20-30			
3959	Lamp base textured	10"h	20-30			
3960	Not used					
3961	Lamp base 'Macklestone' range		20-30			
3962	Lamp base	12"h	20-30			
3963	Extension to lamp	8"h				
3964	Vase wild pigs embossed	10"h	12-18			
3965	Vase embossed	14"l	10-15			
3966	Vase on three feet	9"h	12-20			
3967	Vase on stand		12-20			
3968	Dog Dachshund		25-35			
3969	Vase		5-10			
3970	Vase embossed	9.75"h	15-20			
3971	Wall vase horse shoe		20-25			
3972	Vase	4"h	5-8			
3973	Mug		8-12			
3974	Vase	5"h	5-8			
3975	Tankard 'Wisdom & Providence'	4.25"h	8-12			
3976	Lamp base 'Macklestone' range	10"h	15-25			
3977	Cheese dish 'Totem' range		10-12			
3978	Tankard 'Wisdom and Providence'	5.75h	10-12			

Mould No	Description	Size	Price Guide in £'s	Colour	Date Purchased	Price Paid
3979	Lamp base 'Macklestone' range		20-30			
3980	Vase		5-10			
3981	Coffee mug		8-12			
3982	Honey pot 'Totem' range	4.5"h	5-10			
3983	Vase long		5-10			
3984	Cat		25-35			
3985	Coffee pot		15-20			
3986	Butter dish 'Totem' range	6"l	10-20			
3987	Posy 'Totem' range		3-5			
3988	Dog Irish Terrier	5"h	25-35			
3989	Pot		5-10			
3990	Pot large		8-12			
3991	Tray 'Tulip' range		5-8			
3992	Vase		5-10			
3993	Vase	6"h	5-10			
3994	Vase 'Olympus' range	3.5"h	5-8			
3995	Vase 'Maple' range	10.25"h	12-18			
3996	Ashtray suede cover	5.25"dia	3-6			
3997	Vase	8"h	12-18			
3998	Urn 'Olympus' range	4"h	5-8			
3999	Vase embossed	10"h	18-22			
4000	Vase 'Olympus' range	6"h	8-12			
4001	Vase 'Maple' range	10"l	5-12			

Mould No	Description	Size	Price Guide in £'s	Colour	Date Purchased	Price Paid
4002	Plant pot 'Maple' range	5.25"dia	15-20			
4003	Plant pot fluted		15-20			
4004	Plant pot 'Maple' range	7"dia	15-25			
4005	Pot stone wall effect	3.5"h	10-12			
4006	Plant pot 'Maple' range	5.25"dia	15-20			
4007	Bowl		10-15			
4008	Vase 'Maple' range	7"l	8-12			
4009	Ashtray suede cover		3-6			
4010	Vase 'Maple' range	6"h	5-10			
4011	Vase 'Maple' range	8"h	8-12			
4012	Vase 'Manhattan' range	9"l	12-18			
4013	Bowl 'Maple' range	7.5"dia	10-18			
4014	Condiment set and tray 'Totem' range	3.5"h	15-20			
4015	Bowl		5-10			
4016	Posy vase		5-10			
4017	Bowl round		5-10			
4018	Bowl 'Maple' range	6.75"l	5-10			
4019	Bowl 'Manhattan' range	4"dia	5-10			
4020	Dish 'Totem' for fruit		8-10			
4021	Coffee filter		3-8			
4022	Oil and vinegar set on tray 'Totem' range		6-10			
4023	Posy vase 'Maple' range		5-8			
4024	Bowl 'Manhattan' range	8.5"dia	10-15			

Mould No	Description	Size	Price Guide in £'s	Colour	Date Purchased	Price Paid
4025	Coffee filter.		10-15			
4026	Sugar bowl		5-8			
4027	Ashtray round	6.5"dia	3-5			
4028	Coffee cream jug		5-10			
4029	Toast rack 'Totem' range		5-10			
4030	Cheese board and knife 'Totem' range		10-15			
4031	Four egg cups on stand 'Totem' range		10-15			
4032	Triple tray 'Totem' range	13"l	8-10			
4033	Sugar bowl 'Totem' range	4"dia	3-8			
4034	Beaker 'Totem' range		8-10			
4035	Double tray 'Totem' range		8-10			
4036	Sandwich tray 'Totem' range	13"l	3-6			
4037	Coffee jug 'Totem' range	8.25"h	10-15			
4038	Mug 'Totem' range	4"h	8-10			
4039	Cream jug 'Totem' range	3"h	2-4			
4040	Jug one pint 'Totem' range		5-10			
4041	Storage jar 'Nouveau' range		5-10			
4042	Storage jar 'Nouveau' range small		5-10			
4043	Jug 'Nouveau' range large		15-25			
4044	Jug 'Nouveau' range medium		10-20			
4045	Jug 'Nouveau' range small		8-10			
4046	Tea pot 'Nouveau' large		15-25			
4047	Tea pot 'Nouveau' range small		10-20			

Mould No	Description	Size	Price Guide in £'s	Colour	Date Purchased	Price Paid
4048	Coffee jug 'Nouveau' range		10-15			
4049	Cheese dish 'Nouveau' range		10-15			
4050	Butter dish 'Nouveau' range		10-15			
4051	Sugar bowl 'Nouveau' range		3-8			
4052	Beaker 'Nouveau' range		8-10			
4053	Sugar shaker 'Nouveau' range		8-10			
4054	Honey pot 'Nouveau' range		8-10			
4055	Mixing bowl 'Nouveau' range		15-20			
4056	Mixing bowl 'Nouveau' range small		10-15			
4057	Egg separator 'Nouveau' range		5-8			
4058	Lemon squeezer 'Nouveau' range		5-8			
4059	Condiment set 'Nouveau' range		10-15			
4060	Vinegar bottle 'Nouveau' range		5-8			
4061	Spice jar 'Nouveau' range		5-8			
4062	Not used					
4063	Vase 'Nouveau' range		5-10			
4064	Vase 'Nouveau' range		5-10			
4065	Mug		8-10			
4066	Ashtray		2-5			
4067	Coffee pot		15-20			
4068	Vase acorn and squirrel	8.5"h	30-40			
4069	Vase Stork	10"h	30-40			
4070	Flower jug rabbit climbing	8.5"h	35-45			

Mould No	Description	Size	Price Guide in £'s	Colour	Date Purchased	Price Paid
4071	Double egg cup		5-10			
4072	Coffee filter		5-8			
4073	Beaker		5-8			
4074	Jam pot		8-10			
4075	Honey pot 'Totem' range		8-10			
4076	Coffee pot		15-20			
4077	Cat Manx	3"h	40-55			
4078	Pot square foot		10-15			
4079	Urn vase		5-10			
4080	Urn 'Olympus' range	6.25"h	8-12			
4081	Urn 'Olympus' range	7"h	8-12			
4082	Coffee percolator		15-25			
4083	Pot square foot	11"h	15-18			
4084	Urn 'Olympus' range	9.5"h	10-15			
4085	Bowl square foot		8-12			
4086	Bowl 'Olympus' range	10"dia	10-20			
4087	Cream jug		5-8			
4088	Sugar bowl		5-8			
4089	Cream jug no handle	3.5"h	5-8			
4090	Tankard fish		8-12			
4091	Vase	8"h	12-18			
4092	Vase	10"h	15-20			
4093	Vase 'Olympus' range	8"h	12-18			

Mould No	Description	Size	Price Guide in £'s	Colour	Date Purchased	Price Paid
4094	Lamp base 'Manhattan' range	10"h	20-30			
4095	Tea cup 'Totem' range		3-5			
4096	Vase	5"h	8-12			
4097	Dog King Charles Spaniel	4.75"h	20-35			
4098	Vase 'Olympus' range	10"h	15-20			
4099	Coffee strainer		8-10			
4100	Vase	12"h	15-25			
4101	Coffee filter		5-8			
4102	Coffee filter 'Totem' range		5-8			
4103	Vase 'Olympus' range	5"h	8-12			
4104	Bowl on square foot	7.5"h	12-18			
4105	Vase 'Olympus' range	12"h	15-25			
4106	Coffee pot 'Totem' range	6.25"h	20-25			
4107	Bowl	7.5"dia	8-12			
4108	Mug		8-10			
4109	Bowl embossed	7.5"dia	8-12			
4110	Vase horseshoe horse and Shamrock	4.75"h	5-12			
4111	Posy/ ashtray shamrock	6"l	2-5			
4112	Candleholder	8"h	5-8			
4113	Dog Great Dane	6"h	35-50			
4114	Vase	8"h	10-15			
4115	Bowl 'Olympus' on foot	7"h	10-15			
4116	Vase seaweed and shells	8"h	12-18			

Mould No	Description	Size	Price Guide in £'s	Colour	Date Purchased	Price Paid
4117	Vase floral	8"h	12-18			
4118	Ashtray square	4"sq	2-5			
4119	Vase	8"h	10-15			
4120	Ashtray square	5.5"	2-5			
4121	Vase 'Cornflower'	8"h	12-18			
4122	Bowl square foot		10-15			
4123	Bowl square foot small		8-12			
4124	Jug one pint		15-20			
4125	Ashtray golf		5-8			
4126	Vase embossed	7.5"h	10-15			
4127	Vase 'Sycamore' range	6"h	5-10			
4128	Vase 'Sycamore' range	6.5"h	8-12			
4129	Bowl 'Sycamore' range	8.5"dia	10-18			
4130	Bowl 'Olympus' range	4"h	8-10			
4131	Bowl 'Olympus' range	5"h	8-12			
4132	Plant pot 'Hyacinth' range	7"dia	15-20			
4133	Storage jar		5-10			
4134	Tea pot 'Totem' range		15-25			
4135	Tea pot		15-25			
4136	Ashtray square		2-5			
4137	Tea cup		2-5			
4137	Bowl large		10-20			
4138	Vase	6"h	5-10			

Mould No	Description	Size	Price Guide in £'s	Colour	Date Purchased	Price Paid
4139	Jar spice		5-10			
4140	Tea pot 'Totem' range		15-25			
4141	Saucer 'Totem' range		1-2			
4142	Breakfast cup 'Totem' range		2-5			
4143	Jar storage 'Totem' range	7"h	5-10			
4144	Tea pot 'Totem' range large		20-25			
4145	Ashtray 'Totem' range	4"l	2-5			
4146	Bowl 'Totem' range		8-12			
4147	Bowl 'Totem' range large		10-12			
4148	Jar 'Totem' range spice	3.5"h	5-8			
4149	Cheese dish 'Totem' range	8.25"l	12-18			
4150	Jar 'Totem' range large	8"h	8-12			
4151	Egg separator 'Totem' range		5-8			
4152	Vase 'Marina' range	8"h	10-18			
4153	Plant pot 'Marina' range	7"dia	15-20			
4154	Tray 'Marina' range	6.5"l	8-12			
4155	Plant pot 'Marina' range	4.5"h	12-15			
4156	Plant pot 'Marina' range	5.5"h	15-20			
4157	Vase 'Marina' range	6.25"h	10-15			
4158	Posy 'Marina' range	8"l	8-10			
4159	Plant pot 'Marina' range	8.5"dia	18-25			
4160	Vase 'Marina' range		10-15			
4161	Bowl 'Marina' oval small		10-12			

Mould No	Description	Size	Price Guide in £'s	Colour	Date Purchased	Price Paid
4162	Vase 'Marina' oval small		15-20			
4163	Vase 'Marina' range	5"h	10-12			
4164	Vase 'Flora' range	8"h	10-18			
4165	Vase 'Flora' range	6"h	5-10			
4166	Vase 'Flora' range	9.5"l	5-10			
4167	Posy ring 'Flora' range	6" dia	3-8			
4168	Vase 'Flora' oval large		12-18			
4169	Plant pot 'Flora' range	5.5"h	12-18			
4170	Plant pot 'Flora' range	4.75"h	10-15			
4171	Bowl 'Flora' range		5-10			
4172	Posy 'Flora' range long		5-8			
4173	Bowl 'Flora' on tall foot		10-15			
4174	Vase 'Flora' range	10"h	15-20			
4175	Bowl 'Flora' range	9"dia	10-20			
4176	Sugar shaker 'Totem' range		10-15			
4177	Sauce boat and stand 'Totem' range		8-12			
4178	Posy 'Marina' range		5-8			
4179	Jug 'Totem' range 2 pint	6.25"h	15-20			
4180	Coffee percolator		20-25			
4181	Vase 'Knib' range		5-10			
4182	Egg cups and stand 'Totem' range		12-15			
4183	Tankard half pint		10-12			
4184	Jar Hound head		8-12			

Mould No	Description	Size	Price Guide in £'s	Colour	Date Purchased	Price Paid
4185	Sugar bowl Irish design small		5-10			
4186	Cream jug Irish design		5-8			
4187	Sugar bowl Irish design large		5-8			
4188	Money box pig Irish design		20-30			
4189	Mug		8-10			
4190	Percolator Basket design		15-25			
4191	Beaker		8-10			
4192	Tankard leather cover		8-10			
4193	Sauce boat and stand 'Totem' range		8-12			
4194	Percolator basket design		15-25			
4195	Tray round	6.5"dia	5-8			
4196	Tray triangular		5-8			
4197	Tray square	6.5"	5-8			
4198	Tray oblong		5-8			
4199	Vase crazy paving design	8.5"h	12-18			
4200	Tankard could have pewter effect		10-15			
4201	Plant pot 'Marina' range	4"h	10-15			
4202	Coffee pot 'Totem' range	10.5"h	10-20			
4203	Vase on foot		5-10			
4204	Plant pot 'Marina' range	5"h	1-=15			
4205	Bowl 'Sycamore' range	6.5"l	8-12			
4206	Vase 'Sycamore' range	8"h	8-12			
4207	Vase 'Sycamore' oval		8-12			

Mould No	Description	Size	Price Guide in £'s	Colour	Date Purchased	Price Paid
4208	Vase 'Sycamore' range	10"h	12-18			
4209	Vase 'Sycamore' large		10-18			
4210	Bowl 'Sycamore' range	5"dia	8-12			
4211	Plant pot 'Sycamore' range	5.5"dia	8-12			
4212	Plant pot 'Sycamore' range	6.25"dia	10-15			
4213	Posy 'Sycamore' range		5-10			
4214	Bowl low	6"dia	8-12			
4215	Vase 'Sycamore' range	6"h	8-10			
4216	Sugar bowl		5-8			
4217	Pot stand		3-5			
4218	Covered bowl 'Agincourt' range	4.25"h	8-12			
4219	Not used					
4220	Jar 'Totem' range storage	6.5"h	8-12			
4221	Plate 'Totem' range	10"dia	3-6			
4222	Plate 'Totem' range	8"dia	2-5			
4223	Plate 'Totem' range	6.5"dia	1-3			
4224	Tea pot 'Totem' range	5.75h	15-20			
4225	Lemon squeezer 'Totem' range		5-8			
4226	Vase horseshoe embossed Welsh lady		8-12			
4227	Vase horseshoe embossed Scottie dog		8-12			
4228	Vase horseshoe Devon		8-12			
4229	Vase horseshoe Cornwall		8-12			
4230	Vase horseshoe Somerset		8-12			

Mould No	Description	Size	Price Guide in £'s	Colour	Date Purchased	Price Paid
4231	Posy with deer 'Woodland' range		8-12			
4232	Vase embossed		5-10			
4233	Tree vase 'Woodland' with squirrel	4.5"h	7-12			
4234	Rabbit		20-25			
4235	Coffee pot 'Totem' range		10-20			
4236	Vase horse shoe Cheddar		8-12			
4237	Percolator 'Totem' range	8.75"h	15-25			
4238	N/I					
4239	Posy with deer 'Woodland' range	2.25"h	8-12			
4240	Basket with squirrel 'Woodland' range		10-20			
4240	Basket with deer 'Woodland' range		10-20			
4241	Tree vase 'Woodland' with squirrel	6"h	8-12			
4242	Tree vase 'Woodland' with rabbit	9.25"h	10-20			
4243	Twin tree vase 'Woodland' with rabbit	7"h	8-12			
4244	Tray	7"l	8-12			
4245	Tankard plain	4.5"h	9-15			
4245	Tankard Hereford cider	4.5"h	10-20			
4246	Ashtray horseshoe		3-8			
4247	Lining	7"h	1			
4248	Lining		1			
4249	Tray with small figure		10-15			
4250	Squirrel		20-25			
4251	Dog Corgi	3"h	20-25			

Mould No	Description	Size	Price Guide in £'s	Colour	Date Purchased	Price Paid
4252	Dog Spaniel	3"h	20-25			
4253	Tankard 'Agincourt' range	3.75"h	8-12			
4254	Tankard 'Agincourt' range	4.5"h	8-12			
4255	Tankard 'Agincourt' range	5.5"h	10-15			
4256	Beaker		5-8			
4257	Beaker		5-8			
4258	Vase		5-10			
4259	Coffee jug 'Agincourt' range covered	13.5"h	15-20			
4260	Mug embossed		8-10			
4261	Lining	5"h	1			
4262	Jam pot cauldron with pixie on lid	5"h	8-15			
4263	Vase		5-10			
4264	Vase 'Autumn Chintz' pattern	6"h	8-12			
4265	Plant pot 'Autumn Chintz' pattern	5"h	10-15			
4266	Vase oak leaves	8"h	12-18			
4267	Tankard 'Agincourt' range	6.25"h	10-15			
4268	Jug often pewter colour	5"h	10-15			
4269	Honey jar embossed		8-10			
4270	Tankard 'Agincourt' range	4.25"h	8-12			
4271	Jug for cream 'Agincourt' range	4.25"h	8-12			
4272	Jug 'Agincourt' range	66"h	12-15			
4273	Tankard 'Agincourt' range	4.25"h	8-12			
4274	Tankard 'Agincourt' range	3.5"h	8-12			

Mould No	Description	Size	Price Guide in £'s	Colour	Date Purchased	Price Paid
4275	Tankard 'Agincourt' range	3"h	8-12			
4276	Posy		5-8			
4277	Vase	11"l	15-18			
4278	Bowl		5-10			
4279	Pot		8-12			
4280	Bowl		5-10			
4281	Posy vase	7"l	5-10			
4282	Posy		5-10			
4283	Mug		8-10			
4284	Vase 'Collon No 1' large		25-30			
4285	Vase 'Collon No 2' small		20-25			
4286	Vase 'York'		20-25			
4287	Plant pot with deer 'Woodland' range	4"h	10-18			
4288	Ashtray with deer 'Woodland' range		8-12			
4289	Bowl with squirrel 'Woodland' range	7.5"dia	10-25			
4290	Twin tree vase 'Woodland' with deer	3.25"h	8-12			
4291	Plant pot and squirrel 'Woodland' range	5"h	15-20			
4292	Bowl with rabbit 'Woodland' range		15-20			
4293	Ashtray with deer 'Woodland' range	4.25"l	5-10			
4294	Bowl oval		5-10			
4295	Tankard 'Agincourt' range	5"h	9-15			
4296	Tankard 'Agincourt' range	2.5"h	8-12			
4297	Vase horseshoe embossed pixie	5"h	3-8			

Mould No	Description	Size	Price Guide in £'s	Colour	Date Purchased	Price Paid
4298	Pot 'Harmony' range		8-12			
4299	Vase 'Harmony' range	8"h	8-12			
4300	Posy 'Harmony' range		4-8			
4301	Vase 'Harmony' range	10"h	15-20			
4302	Plant pot 'Harmony' range	7"dia	10-18			
4303	Plant pot 'Harmony' range	6.25"dia	8-15			
4304	Vase10.25"h 'Harmony' range		10-18			
4305	Vase 'Harmony' range small		5-10			
4306	Vase 'Harmony' range	6"h	8-12			
4307	Vase 'Harmony' range large		10-18			
4308	Bowl 'Harmony' range		10-18			
4309	Plant pot 'Harmony' range	7.5"dia	15-20			
4310	Bowl 'Harmony' range	6.25"l	5-10			
4311	Tankard 'Agincourt' range	5.5"h	9-15			
4312	Honey pot		8-12			
4313	Mug 'Totem' range		8-10			
4314	Jam pot embossed		8-10			
4315	Salt and pepper 'Agincourt' range		15-20			
4316	Mustard 'Agincourt' range		8-10			
4317	Tankard 'Agincourt' range	4.25"h	8-12			
4318	Tankard 'Agincourt' range	5.25"h	9-15			
4319	Vase 'Aurora' range	8"h	12-18			
4320	Vase	8"h	10-15			

Mould No	Description	Size	Price Guide in £'s	Colour	Date Purchased	Price Paid
4321	Vase	8"h	10-15			
4322	Vase	8"h	10-15			
4323	Plant pot 'Aurora' range	5"h	10-15			
4324	Plant pot 'Aurora' range	5.5"h	10-20			
4325	Plant pot 'Aurora' range	6"h	10-20			
4326	Plant pot 'Appolo' range	7.5"h	10-20			
4327	Vase 'Aurora' range	6"h	8-12			
4328	Vase 'Aurora' range	10"h	10-20			
4329	Vase 'Aurora' range	4"h	5-10			
4330	Vase 'Aurora' range oval	11"l	10-20			
4331	Vase 'Aurora' range oval		12-18			
4332	Bowl 'Appolo' range oval		8-12			
4333	Percolator		10-20			
4334	Pot 'Manhattan' range		5-10			
4335	Tray shell	6"l	3-8			
4336	Bowl 'Harmony' range	4.25"dia	4-8			
4337	Tray oval		3-8			
4338	Plant pot 'Harmony' range	5"dia	8-12			
4339	Coffee mug	4"h	8-12			
4340	Vase 'Harmony' range	8"h	8-12			
4341	Not used					
4342	Coffee mug embossed	3.75"h	8-12			
4343	Coffee mug 'Oslo' range	3.5"h	8-12			

Mould No	Description	Size	Price Guide in £'s	Colour	Date Purchased	Price Paid
4344	Coffee mug		8-12			
4345	Bowl 'Appolo' range		5-10			
4346	Vase embossed		5-10			
4346	Coffee pot 'Cordon Brun' range		20-25			
4347	Vase		5-10			
4348	Coffee mug embossed leaves	3.75"h	8-12			
4349	Pot 'Olympus' range medium		10-15			
4350	Pot 'Olympus' range small		8-12			
4351	Pot 'Olympus' range large		12-18			
4352	Tankard		9-15			
4353	Number not used					
4354	Tray shell on 3 feet		10-15			
4355	Ashtray horseshoe horses head		5-10			
4356	Plate 'Totem' range oval		3-5			
4357	Plate dinner 'Totem' range oval		4-8			
4358	Open jam pot		3-6			
4359	Tray shell	6"l	3-8			
4360	Money box Pig		20-30			
4361	Money box Owl	4.5"h	20-30			
4362	Mug 'Starway' range		8-12			
4363	Pot		5-10			
4364	Vase	6"h	5-10			
4365	Vase	6"h	5-10			

Mould No	Description	Size	Price Guide in £'s	Colour	Date Purchased	Price Paid
4366	Vase	6"h	5-10			
4367	Vase	8"h	12-18			
4368	Jug 'Agincourt' range	6"h	8-12			
4369	Lining quarter pint		1			
4370	Coffee pot		10-20			
4371	Vase	4"h	5-8			
4372	Cup		3-5			
4373	Vase		5-10			
4374	Vase embossed		5-10			
4375	Vase 'Riverside' range	8"h	10-20			
4375	Posy vase 'Bamboo' range		5-8			
4376	Pot		5-10			
4377	Vase 'Riverside' range	6"h	10-20			
4378	Coffee pot 'Starway' range	10.5"h	15-20			
4379	Vase various ranges		5-10			
4380	Pot		5-10			
4381	Ashtray round	6"dia	2-5			
4382	Sugar bowl		3-5			
4383	Cigarette box rectangular		5-10			
4384	Cream jug 'Starway' range	4"h	5-10			
4385	Vase 'Riverside' range	4"h	10-15			
4386	Beaker		5-8			
4387	Tankard fish head	6"h	15-25			

Mould No	Description	Size	Price Guide in £'s	Colour	Date Purchased	Price Paid
4388	Ashtray 'Evening Fantasy'	4.5"dia	2-4			
4389	Jar tobaco		10-15			
4390	Sugar bowl 'Starway' range	4"dia	5-8			
4391-4392	Not used					
4393	Twin vase 'Riverside' range	3.5"h	8-12			
4394	Bowl 'Riverside' range oval		15-25			
4395	Candle holder 'Riverside' range	2.75"h	5-10			
4396	Candle holder 'Hollyberry' range	2.5"h	8-12			
4397	Ashtray square	4"w	2-5			
4398	Tray 'Hollyberry' range	8"l	15-20			
4399	Tray 'Hollyberry' range	6"l	12-15			
4400	Character jug 'Mine Host' large		25-40			
4401	Character jug 'New Toby'	7.25"h	25-50			
4402	Character jug 'New Toby'	5.25"h	25-40			
4403	Character jug 'New Toby'	3.75"h	15-25			
4404	Character jug 'Old Toby'	8"h	40-50			
4405	Character jug 'Old Toby'	4"h	25-35			
4406	Character jug 'Old Toby'	3"h	15-25			
4407	Character jug 'Coachman'	5.5"h	40-50			
4408	Character jug 'Coachman'	4"h	25-35			
4409	Character jug 'Auld Mac'	4.5"h	25-35			
4410	Character jug 'Auld Mac'	2.5"h	15-20			
4411	Character jug 'Squire'	4"h	25-35			

Mould No	Description	Size	Price Guide in £'s	Colour	Date Purchased	Price Paid
4412	Character jug 'Squire'	2.5"h	25-30			
4413	Character jug 'Jolly Roger' medium		25-40			
4414	Character jug 'Jolly Roger' small		15-25			
4415	Character jug 'Gaffer'	3.75"h	18-30			
4416	Character jug 'Gaffer'	2.5"h	15-25			
4417	Character jug 'Fisherman'	2.25"h	15-25			
4418	Character jug 'Nellie' small		15-25			
4419	Character jug 'James' small		15-25			
4420	Character jug 'Colonel'	3.25"h	15-25			
4421	Character jug 'Silas'	3.25h	15-25			
4422	Character jug 'King Neptune'	4.25"h	18-30			
4423	Character jug 'King Neptune'	3"h	18-30			
4424	Character jug 'King Neptune'	2"h	15-25			
4425	Character jug 'King Neptune' V- large		30-50			
4426	Character jug 'Santa Claus' V- large		30-50			
4427	Character jug 'Santa Claus' large		20-30			
4428	Character jug 'Santa Claus'	3.25"h	15-25			
4429	Character jug 'Santa Claus' small		20-25			
4430	Character jug 'Mr Pickwick' V- large		30-50			
4431	Character jug 'Mr Pickwick'	4.25"h	20-35			
4432	Character jug 'Mr Pickwick'	3.25"h	15-25			
4433	Character jug 'Mr Pickwick'	2"h	20-25			
4434	Character jug 'Tony Weller' V- large		30-50			

Mould No	Description	Size	Price Guide in £'s	Colour	Date Purchased	Price Paid
4435	Character jug 'Tony Weller'	4.5"h	20-35			
4436	Character jug 'Tony Weller'	3.25"h	15-25			
4437	Character jug 'Tony Weller'	2.25"h	15-25			
4438	Character jug 'Sam Weller' V- large		30-50			
4439	Character jug 'Sam Weller'	4.25"h	20-35			
4440	Character jug 'Sam Weller'	3.25"h	15-25			
4441	Character jug 'Sam Weller'	2"h	15-25			
4442	Character jug 'Mrs Bardwell' V- large		30-50			
4443	Character jug 'Mrs Bardwell' large		25-50			
4444	Character jug 'Mrs Bardwell' medium		20-40			
4445	Character jug 'Mrs Bardwell' small		15-25			
4446	Character jug 'Mr Winkle' V- large		30-50			
4447	Character jug 'Mr Winkle'	4.5"h	18-30			
4448	Character jug 'Mr Winkle'	3.25"h	15-25			
4449	Character jug 'Mr Winkle'	2.25"h	15-25			
4450	Character jug 'Watchman'	4.5"h	18-30			
4451	Character jug 'Watchman'	3.5"h	15-25			
4452	Character jug 'Watchman'	2"h	15-25			
4453	Character jug 'Cavalier' medium		50-75			
4454	Character jug 'Cavalier' small		15-25			
4455	Character jug 'George' medium		20-40			
4456	Character jug 'George' small		15-25			
4457	Character jug 'Simon'	3.75"h	20-40			

Mould No	Description	Size	Price Guide in £'s	Colour	Date Purchased	Price Paid
4458	Character jug 'Simon'	2.5"h	15-25			
4459	Character jug 'Mr Wolfe'	3.5"h	20-40			
4460	Character jug 'Mr Wolfe'	2.25"h	15-25			
4461	Character jug 'Mandolin Player' large		25-50			
4462	Character jug 'Mandolin Player'	8"h	30-50			
4463	Character jug 'Mandolin Player' small		15-25			
4464	Character jug 'Louis' small		15-25			
4465	Character jug 'Marie' small		15-25			
4466	Character jug 'Charles'	2.75"h	15-25			
4467	Character jug 'Cabby'	2.75"h	15-25			
4468	Character jug 'Milady' medium		20-40			
4469	Character jug 'Musketeer'	6"h	20-40			
4470	Character jug 'Ann Hathaway'	5.25"h	20-40			
4471	Character jug 'Ann Hathaway'	3"h	15-25			
4472	Character jug 'Ann Hathaway' small		15-25			
4473	Character jug 'William Shakespeare'	4.75"h	20-40			
4474	Character jug 'William Shakespeare'	3"h	15-25			
4475	Character jug small 'William Shakespeare'		15-25			
4476	Character jug 'Churchill'	4.25"h	25-35			
4477	Character jug 'Welsh Lady'	3"h	15-25			
4478	Character jug 'Shylock'	6.5"h	25-50			
4479	Character jug 'Falstaff''	6"h	25050			
4480	Character jug 'Touchstone' large		25-50			

Mould No	Description	Size	Price Guide in £'s	Colour	Date Purchased	Price Paid
4481	Character jug 'Romeo' large		25-50			
4482	Character jug 'Juliet' large		25-50			
4483	Character jug 'Irish Leprechaun' medium		20-40			
4484	Character jug 'Duffy' medium		20-40			
4485	Character jug 'Hamlet'		20-40			
4486	Character jug 'Dick Turpin'	4.75"h	20-40			
4487	Character jug 'Cavalier'	4.75"h	30-40			
4488	Character jug 'Henry VIII'	4"h	20-40			
4489	Character jug 'Yeoman of the Guard'	4.25"h	20-40			
4490	Character jug 'Life Guard'	5"h	20-40			
4491	Character jug 'William Shakespeare'	5"h	30-45			
4492	Character jug 'George Bernard Shaw'	5.5"h	30-45			
4493	Character jug 'Chelsea Pensioner'	4.25"h	15-30			
4494	Character jug 'Grenadier Guard'	5"h	15-30			
4495	Character jug 'Leprechaun'	4.5"h	15-25			
4496	Character jug 'Fisherman'	5"h	20-40			
4497	Character jug 'Harrods Doorman'	4.25"h	30-45			
4498-4499	Not used					
4500	Tea pot Christmas pudding		30-45			
4501	Mug 'Concord'		10-12			
4502	Three piece condiment on stand		15-20			
4503	Sugar bowl		5-8			
4504	Cream jug		5-8			

Mould No	Description	Size	Price Guide in £'s	Colour	Date Purchased	Price Paid
4505	Butter dish oblong		3-5			
4506	Cheese dish		12-18			
4507	Sandwich tray		5-10			
4508	Cup		3-5			
4509	Tray oval	9"l	5-12			
4510	Coffee pot one & half pints		15-25			
4511	Dinner plate oval		5-10			
4512	Coffee pot two & half pints		15-25			
4513	Preserve pot		6-10			
4514	Plate	8"dia	5-8			
4515-4520	Not used					
4521	Plant pot		12-18			
4522	Tea pot		15-20			
4523	Vase 'Rose' range	6"	5-10			
4524	Ashtray 'Riverside' range	4.5" dia	3-8			
4525	Cheese dish with cat and mouse	6.5"l	15-25			
4526	Plant pot 'Rhapsody' range	6.5"dia	10-15			
4527	Ashtray		2-5			
4528	Vase with platform + figure	8.75"h	15-25			
4528	Vase with platform & dog	8.75"h	20-35			
4529	Vase 'Gossamer' range	7"h	10-15			
4530	Honey pot 'Hollyberry' range	4"h	12-18			
4531	Dolphin	8"h	25-35			

Mould No	Description	Size	Price Guide in £'s	Colour	Date Purchased	Price Paid
4532	Vase		5-10			
4533	Not used					
4534	Vase	10"h	18-22			
4535	Vase 'Privet' range	5"h	8-12			
4536	Plant pot 'Privet' range	4"h	5-10			
4537	Vase 'Privet' range	4"h	5-10			
4538	Posy 'Privet' range		3-8			
4539	Plant pot 'Privet' range	3.5"h	10-15			
4540	Vase 'Privet' range	7"h	10-15			
4541	Cream jug in shape of cow		20-25			
4542	Vase 'Adam and Eve'	10"h	18-22			
4543	Butter dish as a cow	7"l	12-20			
4544	Bowl triangular		5-8			
4545	Vase 'Spectrum' range	7.75"h	10-15			
4546	Fox and stand with egg cups		80-130			
4547	Bowl 'Riverside' range	10"dia	30-45			
4548	Vase	8"h	12-18			
4549	Face pot 'Apple sauce'	4.75"h	15-30			
4550	Vase 'Tristan'	6"h	8-12			
4551	Face pot 'Bread sauce'	4"h	35-55			
4552	Vase	6"h	8-12			
4553	Face pot 'Beetroot'	5"h	20-30			
4554	Vase 'Rhapsody' range	8.25"h	10-20			

Mould No	Description	Size	Price Guide in £'s	Colour	Date Purchased	Price Paid
4555	Vase 'Autumn Chintz' oval		10-15			
4556	Vase 'Autumn Chintz' range	10"h	12-22			
4557	Vase 'Autumn Chintz' range	8"h	10-20			
4557	Face pot Bread sauce		20-30			
4558	Vase 'Autumn Chintz' range	6"h	8-12			
4559	Vase 'Autumn Chintz' range	10"w	12-20			
4560	Posy 'Autumn Chintz' range		3-10			
4561	Plant pot 'Gossamer' range	5.5"dia	12-20			
4562	Plant pot 'Tristan' range		12-20			
4563	Vase 'Tristan' range	8"h	10-20			
4564	Vase 'Tristan' range		5-10			
4565	Face pot 'Cucumber'	6"h	25-35			
4566	Tankard fish head	5"h	15-20			
4567	Tankard fish head	4.5"h	15-20			
4568	Vase 'Evening Fantasy' range	8"h	10-15			
4569	Urn 'Evening Fantasy' range	6.26"h	8-12			
4570	Tankard skull	4"h	20-25			
4570	Tea pot skull	4"h	20-30			
4571	Percolator		15-20			
4572	Sauce boat and stand 'Pisces' range		15-20			
4573	Vase 'Assyria' range	8"h	10-20			
4574	Tankard drinking horn	5.75"h	15-22			
4575	Bowl 'Autumn Chintz' range	4.75"dia	8-12			

Mould No	Description	Size	Price Guide in £'s	Colour	Date Purchased	Price Paid
4576	Cheese dish 'Hollyberry' range		25-30			
4577	Three piece condiment 'Hollyberry' & stand		25-30			
4578	Not used					
4579	Posy 'Hollyberry' range		8-12			
4580	Posy ring 'Hollyberry' range		10-15			
4581	Vase 'Tristan' range	10"h	18-22			
4582	Candle stick 'Hollyberry' range		10-15			
4583	Pot 'Tristan' range		5-10			
4584	Tankard boot shaped	5.75"h	15-22			
4585	Salt and pepper		10-15			
4586	Vase 'Tristan' range	6"h	5-10			
4587	Jug with lid 'Starway' range	5.75"h	10-20			
4588	Vase 'Tristan' range	6"h	8-12			
4589	N/I					
4590	Bowl on foot 'Tristan' range round	5"h	10-15			
4591	Bowl 'Tristan' range oval	6"h	10-15			
4592	Vase	6"h	5-10			
4593	Vase 'Tristan' range		12-20			
4594	Vase 'Gossamer' range	9"h	12-20			
4595	Vase 'Tristan' range		5-10			
4596	Plant pot 'Gossamer' range	6.25"dia	15-20			
4597	Vase 'Tristan' range		12-20			
4598	Posy 'Tristan' range	3-6	5-8			

Mould No	Description	Size	Price Guide in £'s	Colour	Date Purchased	Price Paid
4599	Vase 'Gossamer' range	5"h	8-12			
4600	Butter dish barrel with cow on lid	5.25"dia	20-25			
4601	Pot iron bound basket six feet two handles		5-10			
4602	Vase	10"h	18-22			
4603	Vase 'Gossamer' range	9.5"l	12-20			
4604	Bowl 'Gossamer' range	4"dia	8-12			
4605	Posy 'Gossamer' range		5-10			
4606	Vase 'Gossamar' range small		5-10			
4607	Vase oval		5-10			
4608	Vase 'Rhapsody' range	6"h	8-12			
4609	Vase small		8-12			
4610	Vase	10"h	15-22			
4611	Bowl	9.25"l	10-20			
4612	Plant pot 'Rhapsody' range	5.75"dia	10-15			
4613	Plant pot 'Rhapsody' range	8.75"dia	15-25			
4614	Vase 'Rhapsody' oval large		10-20			
4615	Vase 'Rhapsody' oval small		10-15			
4616	Covered bowl 'Pisces' range		15-20			
4617	Vase	10"h	15-22			
4618	Vase	6"h	8-12			
4619	Vase	8"h	10-15			
4620	Bowl 'Rhapsody' range	9"dia	8-15			
4621	Tankard		8-10			

Mould No	Description	Size	Price Guide in £'s	Colour	Date Purchased	Price Paid
4622	Tankard Hound head		8-12			
4623	Tankard Fox head		8-12			
4624	Tankard Horse head		8-12			
4625	Vase	6"h	8-12			
4626	Vase	7"h	10-15			
4627	Lochness monster souvenir		10-15			
4628	Tankard drinking horn	8"h	15-25			
4629	Vase 'Hollyberry' range	6"h	15-25			
4630	Vase	6"h	5-10			
4631	Vase 'Spectrum' range	6"h	5-10			
4632	Tankard riding boot, pint		15-25			
4633	Mug 'Hollyberry' range	3.5"h	10-15			
4634	Tray 'Hollyberry' range	9"l	20-25			
4635	Bowl on foot 'Spectrum' range		5-10			
4636	Vase 'Spectrum' range	10"h	15-22			
4637	Plant pot 'Spectrum' range	6"dia	12-22			
4638	Vase 'Rhapsody' range	10"h	15-22			
4639	Comport 'Rhapsody' range	9"dia	10-15			
4640	Plant pot 'Spectrum' range		12-18			
4641	Bowl 'Rhapsody' range	5.25"h	8-12			
4642	Posy 'Spectrum' range		5-8			
4643	Vase 'Spectrum' range	6.5"l	5-10			
4644	Plant pot 'Spectrum' range	3.5"dia	10-15			

Mould No	Description	Size	Price Guide in £'s	Colour	Date Purchased	Price Paid
4645	Bowl 'Rhapsody' range large		1-12			
4646	Vase 'Hollyberry' range	7.5"w	15-25			
4647	Bowl 'Spectrum' range	5.5"dia	8-12			
4648	Vase 'Spectrum' range	10"w	15-22			
4649	Comport 'Spectrum' range	8.75"dia	10-20			
4650	Badger	4"h	25-35			
4651	Vase 'Spectrum' range	4.75"h	8-12			
4652	Bowl 'Spectrum' range	7"dia	8-12			
4653	Bowl 'Spectrum' range		8-12			
4654	Vase	6"h	5-10			
4655	Vase	6"h	5-10			
4656	Vase	6"h	5-10			
4657	Vase	6"h	5-10			
4658	Vase	6"h	5-10			
4659	Vase	6"h	5-10			
4660	Vase oval small		5-10			
4661	Vase	10"h	15-20			
4662	Vase	10"h	15-20			
4663	Vase	8"h	10-18			
4664	Vase iron bound basket 2 handles 6 feet	8"h	10-18			
4665	Bowl 'Rhapsody' range	4.5"dia	5-8			
4666	Bowl two handles 'Rhapsody' range		10-20			
4667	Flower holder	6"h	5-10			

Mould No	Description	Size	Price Guide in £'s	Colour	Date Purchased	Price Paid
4668	Cup 'Starway' range		2-5			
4669	Salt and pepper 'Pisces' range		20-25			
4670	Bowl round	3.5"h	5-8			
4671	Posy ring	6.5"dia	5-8			
4672	Posy horseshoe shape		5-8			
4673	Posy bar	4.5"l	3-8			
4674	Posy bar	6.75"l	5-10			
4675	Posy bar	8.75"l	8-12			
4676	Posy bar	13.25"l	10-15			
4677	Posy tray		5-10			
4678	Plant pot 'Assyria' range	7"dia	15-25			
4679-4681	Not used					
4682	Mug embossed owl		8-12			
4683	Mint sauce boat on tray leaf design		8-14			
4684	Plate 'Pisces' range	9.5"dia	10-15			
4685	Plate oval 'Pisces' range	12.5"l	12-20			
4686	Tea saucer 'Starway' range		1-2			
4687-4688	Not used					
4689	Vase on foot	8"h	10-15			
4690	Plate 'Assyria' range	12.5"dia	10-15			
4691	Bowl iron bound barrel & handles		10-20			
4692	Vase	6.5"h	8-15			
4693	Vase 'Assyria' range	6.25"h	5-12			

Mould No	Description	Size	Price Guide in £'s	Colour	Date Purchased	Price Paid
4694	Vase	6.5"h	8-15			
4695	Vase	6.5"h	8-15			
4696	Plant pot on three feet		10-15			
4697	Plant pot on three feet		10-15			
4698	Bowl on foot		10-15			
4699	Plant pot 'Assyria' range	5.5"dia	15-20			
4700	Preserve pot		8-12			
4701	Vase	7"h	10-15			
4702	Vase 'Etruscan' range	8"h	12-18			
4703	Tray leaf		5-10			
4704	Vase 'Assyria' range		5-10			
4705	Plate 'Pisces' range	5"dia	8-12			
4706	Plate 'Pisces' range	6.75"dia	10-15			
4707	Horse and rider	9"l	90-130			
4708	Pony and rider	6"l	65-90			
4709	Hound lying down	4"l	15-25			
4710	Hound sniffing	3.5"l	15-25			
4711	Hound on all four	4"l	15-25			
4712	Honey pot golf ball		20-35			
4713	Honey pot foot ball		20-35			
4714	Honey pot cricket ball		20-35			
4715	Honey pot rugby ball		20-35			
4716	Honey pot tennis ball		20-35			

Mould No	Description	Size	Price Guide in £'s	Colour	Date Purchased	Price Paid
4717	Honey pot hocky		20-35			
4718	Honey pot bowls		20-35			
4719	Tankard golf ball	3.75"h	25-35			
4720	Tankard cricket ball	3.75"h	25-35			
4721	Tankard football	3.75"h	25-35			
4722	Tankard rugby ball	4.5"h	25-25			
4723	Tankard tennis	3.75"h	25-35			
4724	Tankard hockey	3.75"h	25-35			
4725	Tankard bowls	3.75"h	25-35			
4726	Tankard capstan	4"h	25-35			
4727	Tankard fishing	3.75"h	25-35			
4728	Tankard soccer	3.75"h	25-35			
4729-4730	Not used					
4731	Bowl on foot		5-10			
4732	Bison	8"l	45-65			
4733	Buffalo	9.5"l	50-90			
4734	Honey pot iron bound basket on six feet		8-12			
4735	Tankard		8-12			
4736	Tankard Thistle	3.75"h	8-12			
4737-4743	Not used					
4744	Jug leaves	4"h	8-15			
4745	Jug Beech leaves	4"h	8-15			
4746	Jug leaves	4"h	8-15			

Mould No	Description	Size	Price Guide in £'s	Colour	Date Purchased	Price Paid
4747	Jug Ash leaves	4"h	8-15			
4748-4749	Not used					
4750	Face pot 'Coleslaw'	4.75"h	70-90			
4751	Face pot 'Tomato'	4.75"h	35-55			
4752	Face pot 'Piccalilli'	5"h	70-80			
4753	Face pot 'Chutney'	5"h	25-40			
4754	Face pot 'Parsley'	4.75"h	50-70			
4755	Face pot 'Pickled cabbage'	5.25"h	45-65			
4756	Face pot 'Onion'	4.75"h	15-25			
4757	Plant pot iron bound basket on six feet	5"dia	12-20			
4758	Bottle	10"h	8-12			
4759	Mint sauce boat		10-15			
4760	Egg separator 'Humpty Dumpty'	4.5"h	35-45			
4761	Bowl round	5"dia	8-12			
4762	Bowl oval	7"dia	10-15			
4763	Plant pot iron bound basket on six feet	4.25"h	12-18			
4764	Plant pot iron bound basket on six feet		15-20			
4765	Stand	3.75" dia	1-2			
4766	Gnome large		20-30			
4767	Spirit measure 'Leather' range		5-10			
4768	Dish thistles Scotland	6"dia	5-10			
4769	Gnome	2.5"h	20-30			
4770	Candle holder 'Chrys' ware		8-12			

Mould No	Description	Size	Price Guide in £'s	Colour	Date Purchased	Price Paid
4771	Ice Jug no handle		8-12			
4772	Vase 'Etruscan' range	6"h	10-15			
4773	Vase 'Etruscan' range	5"h	8-12			
4774	Bowl 'Etruscan' range	4"dia	8-12			
4775	Vase 'Etruscan' range	4"h	5-8			
4776	Plant pot 'Etruscan' range	5.5"dia	12-18			
4777	Plant pot 'Etruscan' range	4.25"dia	10-15			
4778	Plant pot 'Etruscan' range	6.5" dia	15-20			
4779	Bowl 'Etruscan' range	10"dia	10-20			
4780	Bowl 'Etruscan' range	6"dia	8-12			
4781	Bowl 'Etruscan' on foot	7.5"dia	10-15			
4782	Bowl 'Etruscan' on foot		8-12			
4783	Bowl mini 'Etruscan' on foot	2.5"h	8-12			
4784	Vase mini 'Rhapsody' range	2.75"h	8-12			
4785	Jug mini	3"h	8-12			
4786	Vase mini	3"h	8-12			
4787	Vase mini	3"h	8-12			
4788	Jug mini	3"h	8-12			
4789	Vase 'House in the Glen' range	8"h	10-20			
4790	Twin vase 'House in the Glen' range	7"h	8-12			
4791	Vase 'House in the Glen' range	6"h	10-15			
4792	Moustache cup with handle		10-15			
4793	Coffee pot 'Starway' range		15-20			

Mould No	Description	Size	Price Guide in £'s	Colour	Date Purchased	Price Paid
4794	Moustache cup no handle		10-15			
4795	Ice jug with handle		5-12			
4796	Vase	10"h	15-20			
4797	Coffee pot 'Medway' range	8.5"h	15-20			
4798	Bird		20-25			
4799	Vase		5-10			
4800	Vase 'Bamboo' range	8"h	10-15			
4801	Mug 'Medway' range	3.75"h	8-12			
4802	Sugar bowl 'Medway' range	3.5"h	5-8			
4803	Vase	6"h	5-10			
4804	Vase with Dolphin		15-20			
4805	Vase	8"h	10-15			
4806	Cream jug 'Medway' range	4"h	5-8			
4807	Coffee pot 'Brazil' range	8.5"h	20-30			
4808	Vase 'Bamboo' oblong		10-15			
4809	Tea pot 'Croft' range	5.5"h	25-35			
4810	Tankard embossed village	3"h	5-10			
4811	Plate 'Croft' range	8"dia	8-10			
4812	Honey pot 'Croft' range	4.5"h	20-30			
4813	Cream jug 'Croft' range	3"h	15-20			
4814	Sugar bowl 'Croft' range	3.5"dia	15-20			
4815	Cheese dish 'Croft' range		25-30			
4816	Butter dish 'Croft' range		25-30			

Mould No	Description	Size	Price Guide in £'s	Colour	Date Purchased	Price Paid
4817	Mug 'Croft' range	4.5"h	5-10			
4818	Tea cup 'Croft' range		2-44-7			
4819	Saucer 'Croft' range		1			
4820	Plate 'Croft' range	6.5"dia	8-10			
4821	Plate 'Croft' range	8"dia	8-12			
4822	Plate embossed cottage 'Croft'	6.75"dia	10-15			
4823	Plant pot 'Fleur' range	4.75"h	12-18			
4824	Vase oval 'Fleur' range		5-10			
4825	Plant pot 'Fleur' range	4"h	10-15			
4826	Vase oval 'Fleur' range large		12-20			
4827	Vase 'Fleur' range	7"h	10-15			
4828	Vase 'Fleur' range	5"h	8-12			
4829	Vase 'Fleur' range	9"h	12-20			
4830	Bowl 'Fleur' range on foot	5"h	10-15			
4831	Thimble 'Croft' range in box		20-25			
4832	Condiment set 'Croft' 2 or 4 piece		25-35			
4833	Storage jar 'Croft' range	7.5"h	20-25			
4834	Tea pot 'Croft' range	4.75"h	20-35			
4835	Vase leaf with figure		12-28			
4836	Stand with figure		12-20			
4836	Stand with whisky tot		10-15			
4837	Dog Spaniel small		15-20			
4838	Two rabbits small		15-20			

Mould No	Description	Size	Price Guide in £'s	Colour	Date Purchased	Price Paid
4839	Bull Galloway	2..25"h	15-20			
4840	Vase and figure 'Privet' range		10-15			
4841	Top hat with cat and dog		20-25			
4842	Vase		5-10			
4843	Tea cup 'Medway' range		3-5			
4844	Tea saucer 'Medway' range		1-2			
4845	Vase	6"h	8-12			
4846	Dog St Bernard		25-35			
4847	Gnome		20-30			
4848	Bowl 'Bamboo' range		8-12			
4849	Flower holder with picture frame		15-20			
4850	Saucer leaf 'Brazil' range	5.5"dia	3-5			
4851	Tea cup 'Brazil' range		4-7			
4852	Sugar bowl 'Brazil' range	3.5"dia	10-15			
4853	Cream jug 'Brazil' range	4"h	10-15			
4854	Vase rock shape		5-10			
4855	Vase 'Medway' range	5"h	8-12			
4856	Vase 'Medway' range	5"h	8-12			
4857	Vase 'Medway' range	5"h	8-12			
4858	Vase 'Medway' range	7"h	10-15			
4859	Vase 'Medway' range	7"h	10-15			
4860	Vase 'Medway' range	9"h	12-20			
4861	Vase 'Medway' range	6"h	8-12			

Mould No	Description	Size	Price Guide in £'s	Colour	Date Purchased	Price Paid
4862	Vase 'Medway' range	10"h	15-22			
4863	Vase 'Medway' range	7"h	10-15			
4864	Not used					
4865	Preserve pot no lid basket	3"h	8-12			
4866	Preserve lid Strawberry with 4865 or 4871		25-35			
4867	Preserve Lid Blackberry with 4865 or 4871		25-35			
4867	Preserve Lid Raspberry with 4865 or 4871		25-35			
4868	Preserve lid Plum with 4865 or 4871		25-35			
4869	Not used					
4870	Not used					
4871	Preserve pot no lid leaf	2.75"h	3-8			
4872	Horse Shire with harness		40-60			
4873	Horse Shire no harness		30-40			
4873	Tankard boot		10-15			
4874	Salt and pepper 'Medway' range		5-10			
4875	Plate 'Medway' range	6.75"dia	3-6			
4876	Preserve 'Medway' range	4.5"h	5-10			
4877	Cheese dish 'Medway' range		8-15			
4878	Dinner plate 'Medway' oval		4-8			
4879	Soup bowl 'Medway' range	5.5"dia	2-4			
4880	Tea pot 'Medway' range		15-20			
4881	Sandwich tray 'Medway' range		3-8			
4882	Butter dish 'Medway' range		8-15			

Mould No	Description	Size	Price Guide in £'s	Colour	Date Purchased	Price Paid
4883	Not used					
4884	Vase	7"h	10-15			
4885	Log with Blue tits		20-35			
4886	Bowl 'House in the Glen' range	8"l	10-20			
4887	Basket 'House in the Glen' range	5.5"l	15-25			
4888	Tray 'House in the Glen' range		5-10			
4889	Posy round 'House in the Glen' range	8.5"dia	15-25			
4890	Posy 'House in the Glen'		10-15			
4891-4894	Not used					
4895	Face pot 'Lemon'	4.5"h	40-60			
4896	Face pot 'Orange'	3.5"h	40-60			
4897	Face pot 'Plum'		50-70			
4898	Face pot 'Blackberry'	3.75"h	50-70			
4898	Face pot 'Raspberry'	3.75"h	50-70			
4899	Face pot 'Strawberry'	3.5"h	35-50			
4900	Not used					
4901	Cereal bowl		4-6			
4902	Beef dripping holder	3.5"h	15-25			
4903	Pork dripping holder	3.5"h	15-25			
4904	Lard holder	3.5"h	15-25			
4905	Soup bowl		9-15			
4906	Face pot 'Pan scourer' lid	3.25"h	20-30			
4906	Face pot 'Beef stock cubes' lid	3.25"h	20-30			

Mould No	Description	Size	Price Guide in £'s	Colour	Date Purchased	Price Paid
4906	Face pot 'Chicken stock' lid	3.25"h	20-30			
4907	Sink tidy bowl		35-45			
4908	Soup bowl and lid embossed vegetables		25-35			
4909-4912	Not used					
4913	Bowl for bath salts		8-12			
4914	Mug fish		8-12			
4915	Face pot 'Tartare sauce'	3.75"h	65-90			
4916	Soap dish fish shape		10-12			
4917	Toilet roll holder		8-12			
4918	Talcum powder holder		8-12			
4919	Tooth brush holder fish shape		10-15			
4920	Not used					
4921	Plant pot hexagonal		15-25			
4922	Plant pot hexagonal medium		12-20			
4923	Plant pot hexagonal small		10-15			
4924	Shaving tankard		10-15			
4925	Shaving tankard		10-15			
4926	Shaving tankard		10-15			
4927	Shaving tankard		10-15			
4928	Rabbit used as additional ornaments	2"h	20-30			
4929	Pixie used as additional ornaments		20-30			
4930	Swan used as additional ornaments		20-30			
4931	Tea pot shape strainer and stand complete		15-25			

Mould No	Description	Size	Price Guide in £'s	Colour	Date Purchased	Price Paid
4932	Vase		12-20			
4933	Vase mushroom shape		12-20			
4934	Vase mushroom shape	5"h	8-12			
4935	Vase mushroom shape	6.5"h	10-15			
4936	Vase		5-10			
4937-4944	Not used					
4945	Ashtray coffin		10-15			
4946	Vase	5"h	8-12			
4947	Vase		5-10			
4948	Vase	10"h	15-20			
4949	Bowl		5-10			
4950	Vase on square foot	7"h	10-15			
4951	Basket etched floral		10-15			
4952	Vase etched	8"h	10-20			
4953-4958	Not used					
4959	Tankard		8-12			
4960	Tankard		8-12			
4961	Tankard		8-12			
4962	Tankard		8-12			
4963	Horse Shire	7"h	25-40			
4964	Shaving mug	3.75"h	10-15			
4965	Denture holder 'Mosaic' range	3"h	15-20			
4966	Bath salts holder 'Mosaic' range		15-26			

Mould No	Description	Size	Price Guide in £'s	Colour	Date Purchased	Price Paid
4967	Mug 'Mosaic' range	3.75"h	10-15			
4968	Soap tray 'Mosaic' range		8-12			
4969	Toilet roll holder 'Mosaic' range	4.25"h	15-20			
4970	Tooth brush holder 'Mosaic' range	4"h	15-20			
4971	Shaving mug 'Mosaic' range	4"h	15-25			
4972	Tray/stand for Galloway bull not available					
4973	Boy and dog not known					
4974	Pomander chicken		10-15			
4975	Pomander floral ball		10-15			
4976	Bookends ships lanterns	5.75"h	60-80			
4977	Kittens in boot	4.5"h	10-15			
4978	Horse Shire	7"h	25-40			
4979	Vase embossed basket		8-12			
4980-4985	Not used					
4986	Dog Dachshund	7.75"l	20-35			
4987	Basket	4"h	5-10			
4988	Dog West Highland Terrier	6.25"l	25-35			
4989	Pomander frog	2.5"h	15-25			
4990	Pomander mouse		15-25			
4991	Pomander squirrel		15-25			
4992	Dog Boxer	5"h	25-35			
4993	Vase 'Florence' range	4.75"h	10-18			
4994	Vase 'Florence' range	4.75"h	10-18			

Mould No	Description	Size	Price Guide in £'s	Colour	Date Purchased	Price Paid
4995	Vase 'Florence' grapevine	4.75"h	10-18			
4996	Vase 'Florence' 2 handle	4.5"h	10-18			
4997	Vase 'Florence' range	4.75"h	10-18			
4998	Vase 'Florence' cottage	4.75"h	10-18			
4999	Dog Spaniel standing		25-35			
5000	Dog Collie	9"l	25-35			
5001	Saucer embossed rose		1-3			
5002	Cup embossed rose		3-5			
5003	Vase 'Churnet' range	8"h	10-20			
5004	Vase 'Churnet' range	6"h	8-12			
5005	Plant pot 'Churnet' range	5"h	10-15			
5006	Plant pot 'Churnet' range	5.5"h	12-18			
5007	Vase 'Churnet' range	10"h	15-20			
5008	Plant pot 'Churnet' range	5"h	10-15			
5009	Bowl 'Churnet' range	7"h	8-12			
5010	Plant pot 'Churnet' range	7"h	15-20			
5011	Plinth for 5010 'Churnet' range not available					
5012-5014	Not used					
5015	Vase 'Milton' range	8"	12-18			
5016-5018	Not used					
5019	Pot	7"dia	10-20			
5020	Bowl		5-10			
5021	Bowl	5"h	5-10			

Mould No	Description	Size	Price Guide in £'s	Colour	Date Purchased	Price Paid
5022	Rose bowl and cover		10-20			
5023	Dog Shetland sheepdog	6.25"h	20-35			
5024	Dog Shetland sheepdog	7"h	25-40			
5025	Dog Poodle sitting	11.25"h	30-50			
5026	Vase	5.5"h	8-12			
5027	Dog Yorkshire Terrier	5.5"h	15-25			
5028	Posy log with Kingfisher		10-15			
5029	Flower holder 'Pebble' range		10-15			
5030	Tankard half pint 'Coco de Mer'		8-12			
5031	Dog Poodle sitting	8.5"h	25-35			
5032	Dog Boxer	7.5"l	30-40			
5033	Jug embossed celery	7.5"h	25-35			
5034	Dog Dalmation	9"l	30-40			
5035	Horse hunter standing	11.5"h	65-80			
5036	Money box dog		20-30			
5037	Money box frog		20-30			
5038	Tea bag holder	6"l	15-25			
5039	Money box Owl	8"h	20-30			
5040	Eagle		90-130			
5041	Coffee bag holder	6"l	15-25			
5042	Kitchen vase embossed spring onions	4.5"h	10-15			
5043	Dish embossed corn on cob	9"l	8-12			
5044-5046	N/I					

Mould No	Description	Size	Price Guide in £'s	Colour	Date Purchased	Price Paid
5047	Tea bag dispenser		10-15			
5048	Face pot 'Horseradish'	4.25"h	65-90			
5049	Dog Beagle	8.5"l	30-45			
5050	Pie funnel swans		15-20			
5051	Vase etched	6"h	5-12			
5052	Thimble pigs head with box		20-25			
5053	Thimble castle with box		20-25			
5054	Thimble Rose with box		20-25			
5055	Thimble Daffodil with box		20-25			
5056	Thimble heart with box		20-25			
5057	Thimble Leaning tower of Pisa with box		20-25			
5058	Thimble windmill with box		20-25			
5059	Thimble circus clown with box		20-25			
5060	Thimble 'Wishing Well' with box		20-25			
5061	Thimble unicorn with box		20-25			
5062	Thimble lion with box		20-25			
5063	Cigarette box chest	4.25"w	10-15			
5064	Ashtray		8-10			
5065	Ashtray ships wheel		8-10			
5066	Vase 'Trentham' range	5"h	5-10			
5067	Vase 'Trentham' range	8"h	10-15			
5068	Vase 'Trentham' range	5.25"h	5-10			
5069	Plant pot 'Trentham' range	5"h	10-15			

Mould No	Description	Size	Price Guide in £'s	Colour	Date Purchased	Price Paid
5070	Plant pot 'Trentham' range	6"h	12-18			
5071	Vase 'Trentham' range	7.75"h	10-15			
5072	Bowl 'Trentham' on foot	6"h	8-12			
5073	Bowl 'Trentham' low round		8-15			
5074	Dish/bowl 'Trentham' range		8-12			
5075	Vase 'Trentham' range	4.25"h	5-8			
5076	Dog Spaniel	7.75"l	20-35			
5077	Coffee bag holder		15-20			
5078	Tea cup		2-5			
5079	Tea saucer		1-3			
5080	Plate	6.5"dia	4-6			
5081	Sugar bowl	3.25"h	2-5			
5082	Cream jug	3.75"h	3-6			
5083	Coffee pot	9"h	15-20			
5084	Plate bread and butter	11"dia	10-15			
5085	Sandwich tray	12.5"l	5-10			
5086	Salt and pepper		8-12			
5087	Tea pot	5"h	15-20			
5088	Tea pot	5.75"h	15-25			
5089	Cream jug individual		2-4			
5090	Tankard	4.25"h	8-10			
5091	Money box tortoise	5.75"l	15-25			
5092	Money box owl	4.75"h	15-25			

Mould No	Description	Size	Price Guide in £'s	Colour	Date Purchased	Price Paid
5093	Money box squirrel	5.75"h	20-30			
5094-5095	Not used					
5096	Money box Bulldog	5.75"h	20-30			
5097	Money box frog	5.25"h	15-25			
5098	Tankard half pint		8-15			
5099	Tankard moustache	3.75"h	10-15			
5100	Pen tray		8-10			
5101	Money box caricature tortoise		12-25			
5102	Money box caricature elephant		25-35			
5103	Money box caricature Bloodhound		15-25			
5104	Money box with eyes Teddy bear without eyes		15-35 15-25			
5105	Money box caricature Chipmunk		15-20			
5106	Money box caricature owl		15-25			
5107	Cat Siamese	8.5"l	45-65			
5108	Dog Afghan hound	8.75"l	30-40			
5109	Bowl cucumber		5-8			
5110	Grapefruit bowl on stand		5-10			
5111	Cat Siamese	8.75"h	45-65			
5112	Dog Alsation	8.5"l	25-40			
5113	Character jug 'Friar Tuck'	6.75"h	40-50			
5114	Character jug 'Robin Hood'	6"h	40-50			
5115	Character jug 'Sheriff of Nottingham'	6"h	40-50			
5116	Character jug 'Little John'	6.75"h	40-50			

Mould No	Description	Size	Price Guide in £'s	Colour	Date Purchased	Price Paid
5117	Character jug 'Maid Marion'	6.25"h	40-50			
5118	Character jug 'Allan A Dale'	6.25"h	40-50			
5119	Duck Mallard	6.5"l	30-40			
5120	Duck Golden Eye	6"l	30-40			
5121	Gosling		20-30			
5122	Duck Shoveller	6.5"l	30-40			
5123	Duck Tufted		30-40			
5124	Mug		8-12			
5125	Horse Shire	8.75"l	25-35			
5126	Face pot 'Onion'	4"h	20-35			
5127	Face pot 'Beetroot'	4"h	30-55			
5128	Strawberry bowl		10-20			
5129	Raspberry bowl		10-20			
5130	Ashtray with cover		2-5			
5131	Donkey		50-80			
5131	Donkey with baskets or saddle		50-80			
5132	Vase 'Florence' range	7.5"h	10-15			
5133	Vase 'Florence' range	2,75"h	5-8			
5134	Vase 'Florence' range	9"h	12-20			
5135	Plant pot 'Florence' range	5.5"h	8-12			
5136	Candle holder 'Florence' range		5-10			
5137	Plant pot 'Florence' range	4.5"h	10-15			
5138	Twin candle holder 'Florence' range	2.75"h	8-12			

Mould No	Description	Size	Price Guide in £'s	Colour	Date Purchased	Price Paid
5139	N/I					
5140	Bowl 'Florence' on foot		8-12			
5141	Not used					
5142	Vase 'Florence' range oval		10-15			
5143	Ham stand for Rodek		5-10			
5144	Ashtray for Rodek		3-5			
5145	Ashtray for Lesney with sand buggy		20-30			
5146	Ashtray for Lesney with aeroplane		20-25			
5147	Covered muffin dish and stand		10-15			
5148	Jug and stand leaf for mayonnaise		10-18			
5149	Pomander 'Mr Pickwick'		20-30			
5150	Dog Dobermann	8.5"l	30-40			
5151	Tray for banana split		10-12			
5152	Elephant	5"l	25-35			
5153	Coffee mug series		4-8			
5154	Coffee mug series		4-8			
5155	Coffee mug series		4-8			
5156	Coffee mug series		4-8			
5157	Coffee mug series		4-8			
5158	Coffee mug series		4-8			
5159	Coffee mug series		4-8			
5160	Coffee mug series		4-8			
5161	Coffee mug series		4-8			

Mould No	Description	Size	Price Guide in £'s	Colour	Date Purchased	Price Paid
5162	Coffee mug series		4-8			
5163	Coffee mug series		4-8			
5164	Not used					
5165	Bust Winston Churchill	8"h	45-50			
5166	Rhinoceros	10.5"l	100-125			
5167	Dog Labrador	9.5"l	20-35			
5168	Butter dish sunflower lid	5"dia	10-15			
5169	Butter dish oblong sunflower lid	6"l	15-25			
5170	Dog Setter	9.25"l	30-40			
5171	Coffee pot 'Alton' range		15-20			
5172	Cream jug 'Alton' range	4"h	4-6			
5173	Tea cup 'Alton' range		3-5			
5174	Salt and pepper 'Alton' range		8-12			
5175	Sugar bowl 'Alton' range	3.5"dia	3-5			
5176	Tea saucer 'Alton' range		1-2			
5177	Plate 'Alton' range	6.75"dia	3-10			
5179	Plate bread and butter	10.5"dia	8-12			
5180	Butter dish 'Alton' range	5.25"l	10-15			
5181	Cheese dish 'Alton' range		10-15			
5182	Preserve pot 'Alton' range	4.75"h	5-10			
5183	Cereal bowl 'Alton' range	6.5"dia	3-8			
5184	Not used					
5185	Bowl 'Dolphin' range	7.5"l	18-25			

Mould No	Description	Size	Price Guide in £'s	Colour	Date Purchased	Price Paid
5186	Vase 'Dolphin' range	4"h	15-20			
5187	Tray 'Dolphin' range		10-15			
5188	Vase 'Dolphin' range	5.75"h	15-25			
5189	Plant pot 'Dolphin' range	4"h	15-25			
5190	Posy vase 'Dolphin' range		12-18			
5191	Basket 'Dolphin' range		10-20			
5192	Twin vase 'Dolphin' range	3.25"h	10-20			
5193	Bowl	2.5"h	4-6			
5194	Dog's bowl embossed head, bones etc lid	5"dia	50-65			
5195	Cat's bowl embossed head, fish etc lid	5"dia	85-110			
5196	Vase		5-10			
5197	Bull Galloway	5"h	60-80			
5198	Character jug fisherman	5"h	20-40			
5199	Character jug clerk	5"h	20-40			
5200	Character jug horse dealer		20-40			
5201	Character jug coal miner	5"h	20-40			
5202	Character jug bricklayer		20-40			
5203	Character jug cook		20-40			
5204	Coffee mug	4"h	4-8			
5205	Dog Welsh Sheepdog	9.5"l	30-40			
5206	Character jug John F Kenedy	6"h	35-45			
5207	Bull Galloway	4.75"h	45-65			
5208	Mug with face		10-15			

Mould No	Description	Size	Price Guide in £'s	Colour	Date Purchased	Price Paid
5209	Fox 'Prestige' range	10.5"l	45-80			
5210	Gazelle 'Modus' range	9.5"l	30-40			
5211	Squirrel 'Prestige' range	7"l	50-80			
5212	Cheetah 'Modus' range	10"l	30-45			
5213	Horse 'Modus' range	8.5"l	30-45			
5214	Loving cup three handles		5-10			
5215	Character mug 'George Washington'		20-40			
5216	Badger with rock	5"h	20-35			
5217	Tankard	4"h	4-8			
5218	Tankard	4"h	5-8			
5219	Tankard	4"h	5-8			
5220	Not used					
5221	Tankard Volvo		10-15			
5222	Character tankard Indian 'Benskins' limited edition	5.75"h	60-80			
5223	Vase embossed	8"h	10-15			
5224	Vase embossed	8"h	10-15			
5225	Vase	8"h	10-15			
5226	Vase	10"h	15-20			
5227	Vase	7"h	10-15			
5228	Vase	6"h	8-12			
5229	Hippopotamus	6"l	15-25			
5230	Camel	5"l	20-30			
5231	Bear	6"l	30-40			

Mould No	Description	Size	Price Guide in £'s	Colour	Date Purchased	Price Paid
5232	Two monkeys	4"h	20-30			
5233	Lion	6.25"l	20-30			
5234	Giraffe	5"h	20-30			
5235	Cushion not available without cat					
5236	Cat long haired	8.25"l	40-55			
5237	Cat	11.5"l	40-55			
5238	Polar Bear 'Modus' range	7"h	30-45			
5239	Badger	5.5"h	25-35			
5240	Plant pot	6.25"h	10-20			
5241	Cup		3-5			
5242	Holder for washing up brush	6"h	25-35			
5243	Flower jug 'Harvest Time' range	7.75"h	20-35			
5244	Basket 'Harvest Time' range		15-25			
5245	Plant pot 'Harvest Time' range	5"h	20-30			
5246	Jug 'Harvest Time' range	4.5"h	15-25			
5247	Twin vase 'Harvest Time' range	6"h	15-25			
5248	Bowl small 'Harvest Time' range	5"l	15-25			
5249	Bowl 'Harvest Time' range	6"dia	20-30			
5250	Vase oval medium 'Harvest Time' range		20-30			
5251	Mouse used as additional ornaments	2.5"h	— —			
5252	Mouse used as additional ornaments	1.75"h	— —			
5253	Not used					
5254	Mouse used as additional ornaments		— —			

Mould No	Description	Size	Price Guide in £'s	Colour	Date Purchased	Price Paid
5255	Fox used as additional ornaments		— —			
5256	Vase	6"h	8-12			
5257	Rabbit used as additional ornament		— —			
5258	Dog Great Dane 'Supreme' range	9"l	30-40			
5259	Dog Schnauzer 'Supreme' range	7"l	30-40			
5260	Dog Whippet 'Supreme' range	6"l	30-40			
5261	Cat hunting	10.5"l	40-55			
5262	Cat sitting	7"l	40-55			
5263	Dog Poodle standing	5.5"h	25-35			
5264-5265	Not used					
5266	N/I					
5267	Vase	5.5"h	8-12			
5268	Vase etched	7"h	10-15			
5269	Vase etched	6.5"h	8-12			
5270	Tankard half pint	4.25"h	8-10			
5271	Tankard quarter pint	3.25"h	4-8			
5272	Covered bowl plain	4.25"dia	5-10			
5273	Bowl 'Rhapsody' range		5-10			
5274	Bowl 'Vintage' range	7.75"dia	8-12			
5275	Urn 'Vintage' range	9"h	18-22			
5276	Plant pot 'Vintage' range	7"h	10-15			
5277	Comport 'vintage' range	10.5"dia	10-20			
5278	Vase 'Vintage' range	7"h	10-15			

Mould No	Description	Size	Price Guide in £'s	Colour	Date Purchased	Price Paid
5279	Vase 'Bamboo' range		5-10			
5280	Urn 'Vintage' range	9"h	12-20			
5281	Tankard	5.75"h	10-20			
5282	Tankard	8"h	10-20			
5283	Tankard to fit holder quarter pint		8-10			
5284	Tankard		8-15			
5285	Leaf		5-10			
5286	Bowl for dish cloth		30-45			
5287	Eagle	8"h	25-35			
5288	Ashtray Geest		3-6			
5289	Lop eared rabbit 'Thumper'	7"h	20-30			
5290	Lop eared rabbit 'Thumper'	5.25"h	15-25			
5291	Lop eared rabbit 'Thumper'	4"h	15-20			
5292	Dog caricature	7"h	20-30			
5293	Dog caricature	5.5"h	15-25			
5294	Dog caricature	4"h	10-20			
5295	Dog caricature	7"h	20-30			
5296	Dog caricature	5.25"h	15-25			
5297	Dog caricature	3.75"h	10-20			
5298	Cat caricature	7"h	20-30			
5299	Cat caricature	5.25"h	15-25			
5300	Cat caricature	4"h	15-20			
5301	Sheep dog caricature	7"h	20-30			

Mould No	Description	Size	Price Guide in £'s	Colour	Date Purchased	Price Paid
5302	Sheep dog caricature	5.25"h	15-25			
5303	Sheep dog caricature	3.75"h	15-20			
5304	Dog Corgi	7.5"h	25-30			
5305	Rabbit large more info needed					
5306	Rabbit medium more info needed					
5307	Rabbit small more info needed					
5308	Pot for tea bags	4.5"h	20-25			
5309	Ashtray square	5.75"l	2-5			
5310	Ashtray oblong		2-5			
5311	Ashtray oval		2-5			
5312	Dog Corgi		25-35			
5313	Staffordshire Rustics 'Emily with dog'	10"h	60-75			
5314	Staffordshire Rustics 'Alice with goat'		60-75			
5315	Staffordshire Rustics 'Adam the Gamekeeper'		60-75			
5316	Staffordshire Rustics 'Katie the Goosegirl'		60-75			
5317	Candlestick	6"h	5-10			
5318	Candlestick embossed	6"h	5-10			
5319	Dog Chihuahua 'Supreme' range	5.75"h	25-35			
5320	Dog St Burnard 'Supreme' range	9.5"l	30-40			
5321	Dog Corgi 'Supreme' range	6.75"l	20-35			
5322	Dog Old English Sheepdog 'Supreme' range	7"l	20-35			
5323	Dog Sealyham 'Supreme' range	7.5"l	25-35			
5324	Dog Pyrennean Mountain 'Supreme' range		35-40			

Mould No	Description	Size	Price Guide in £'s	Colour	Date Purchased	Price Paid
5325	Jug 'New Cavalier' range	8"h	30-50			
5326	Punch bowl 'New Cavalier' range	10.5"dia	20-30			
5327	Wall plaque 'New Cavalier' range		20-30			
5328	Tankard 'New Cavalier' range	5.75"h	18-25			
5329	Jug 'New Cavalier' range	6"h	10-20			
5330	Wine goblet 'New Cavalier' range	5"h	10-20			
5331	Ashtray 'New Cavalier' range		3-6			
5332	Loving cup 'New Cavalier' range		10-15			
5333	Tankard 'New Cavalier' range	4"h	8-12			
5334	Decanter 'New Cavalier' range		15-20			
5335	Hanging bowl 'Right Herbert'		20-30			
5336	Hanging bowl 'Right Herbert' large		25-40			
5337	Jug 'Cordon Brun' range	6.25"h	10-15			
5338	Jug 'Cordon Brun' range	5.5"h	10-12			
5339	Jug 'Cordon Brun' range	4.75"h	10-15			
5340	Jug 'Cordon Brun' range	3.75"h	8-10			
5341	Storage jar 'Cordon Brun' range	6.75"h	10-18			
5342	Storage jar 'Cordon Brun' range	5"h	10-12			
5343	Salt and pepper 'Cordon Brun' range		10-15			
5344	Salt jar 'Cordon Brun' range	7.5"h	15-20			
5345	Preserve pot 'Cordon Brun' range	4"h	10-15			
5347	Tea pot 'Cordon Brun' range		15-25			
5348	Mug 'Cordon Brun' range		8-10			

Mould No	Description	Size	Price Guide in £'s	Colour	Date Purchased	Price Paid
5349	Butter dish 'Cordon Brun' range		10-15			
5350	Cheese dish 'Cordon Brun' range	7.25"l	15-20			
5351	Preserve pot holder 'Cordon Brun' range		2-4			
5352	Tea cup 'Cordon Brun' range		2-5			
5353	Tea saucer 'Cordon Brun' range		1-3			
5354	Plate 'Cordon Brun' range	6.5"dia	3-6			
5355	Plate 'Cordon Brun' range	8"dia	4-8			
5356	Egg cup with saucer 'Cordon Brun' range		5-10			
5357	Sugar sifter 'Cordon Brun' range	5.25"h	10-15			
5358	Spoon rest 'Cordon Brun' range		8-15			
5359	Egg separator 'Cordon Brun' range		8-10			
5360	Lemon squeezer 'Cordon Brun' range		8-10			
5361	Spice jar 'Cordon Brun' range	3.75"h	10-15			
5362	Bowl 'Cordon Brun' range	6.5"dia	8-12			
5363	Comport 'Cordon Brun' range	6"h	15-22			
5364	Double egg cup 'Cordon Brun' range		8-12			
5365	Teapot stand 'Cordon Brun' range		1-3			
5366	Toast rack 'Cordon Brun' range		1-15			
5367	Ashtray		2-5			
5368	Ashtray		2-5			
5369	Plant pot 'Bamboo' range	5.25"dia	12-18			
5370	Vase 'Bamboo' range	7.75"h	10-15			
5371	Plant pot 'Bamboo' range	6.5"dia	15-20			

Mould No	Description	Size	Price Guide in £'s	Colour	Date Purchased	Price Paid
5372	Vase 'Bamboo' range	10"h	15-20			
5373	Vase 'Bamboo' range	12"h	15-25			
5374	Vase 'Bamboo' range	6"h	5-10			
5375	Posy 'Bamboo' range	8"l	5-10			
5376	Posy vase 'Bamboo' range	11"l	5-10			
5377	Posy vase 'Bamboo' range	5.75"l	3-6			
5378	Plant pot 'Bamboo' range	7.5"dia	15-20			
5379	Plant pot 'Bamboo' range	8.75"dia	15-20			
5380	Dog English Sheepdog		25-35			
5381	Dog Skye Terrier	3.5"h	25-35			
5382	Ashtray horseshoe		3-5			
5383	Honey pot a bee	5"h	30-40			
5384	Ashtray		2-4			
5385	Pomander		8-10			
5386	Tray 'Lincoln' range	7.25"l	2-5			
5387	Vase 'Lincoln' range	8"h	10-15			
5388	Jug 'Lincoln' range	8"h	12-18			
5389	Plant pot handles 'Lincoln' range	5.75"h	15-20			
5390	Bowl large 'Lincoln' range	12.5"l	12-20			
5391	Vase 'Lincoln' range	10"h	15-20			
5392	Vase	8"h	10-15			
5393	Ginger jar 'Canton' range	11.5"h	30-40			
5394	Ginger jar 'Canton' range	9.5"h	25-30			

Mould No	Description	Size	Price Guide in £'s	Colour	Date Purchased	Price Paid
5395	Ginger jar 'Canton' range	7"h	20-25			
5396	Jar 'Canton' range	13"h	40-50			
5397	Jar 'Canton' range	9"h	25-35			
5398	Covered bowl 'Canton' range	9"h	25-35			
5399	Covered bowl 'Canton' range	9.5"dia	25-35			
5400	Salt and pepper 'Severn' shape		8-12			
5401	Jar for bath salts made for Boots	7"h	10-15			
5402	Cheese dish 'Severn' shape	8.75"l	10-20			
5403	Ashtray		2-5			
5404	Leyland lorry limited edition		150-200			
5405	Ashtray		2-5			
5406	Bowl	5"h	8-12			
5407	Ashtray		2-5			
5408	Tray		5-10			
5409	Tea pot 'English Rose' range	5"h	15-20			
5410	Sugar bowl 'English Rose' range		3-6			
5411	Cream jug 'English Rose' range		4-8			
5412	Tea saucer 'English Rose' range		1-2			
5413	Plate 'English Rose' range	6.75"dia	3-6			
5414	Tea cup 'English Rose' range		3-5			
5415	Salt and pepper 'English Rose' range		8-12			
5416	Preserve pot 'English Rose' range		8-12			
5417	Cheese dish 'English Rose' range		10-15			

Mould No	Description	Size	Price Guide in £'s	Colour	Date Purchased	Price Paid
5418	Butter dish 'English Rose' range		10-15			
5419	Tea pot 'Severn' shape	5.5"h	15-20			
5420	Jug No 4 'Severn' shape	4"h	5-10			
5421	Mug		4-8			
5422	Honey pot	5"h	8-12			
5423	Tea Time set clock face tea pot and mug		40-60			
5424	Butter dish	5.75"l	10-15			
5425	Tea pot 'Three Tea Bag Pot'	5.5"h	30-40			
5426	Tea pot 'Two Tea Bag Pot'	4.75"h	20-30			
5427	Tea pot 'One Tea Bag Pot'	4"h	10-20			
5428	Tea pot stand	6"dia	5-10			
5429	Jug No 3 'Severn' shape	4.5"h	8-12			
5430	Jug No 2 'Severn' shape	4.75"h	8-12			
5431	Lamp base owl	4.24"h	20-25			
5432	Lamp base tortoise	3.5"h	20-25			
5433	Lamp base hound	5"h	20-25			
5434	Dog Springer Spaniel	8"l	25-35			
5435	Jug 'Pipers Whisky' limited edition		20-25			
5436	Ashtray 'Pipers Whisky' limited edition		10-15			
5437	Ashtray 'Guinness' limited edition		10-15			
5438	Bell with dove		10-15			
5439	Soap dish		8-10			
5440	Ashtray tyre		4-8			

Mould No	Description	Size	Price Guide in £'s	Colour	Date Purchased	Price Paid
5441	Jug & Teapot minature 'Hollington' range	3"h	15-25			
5442	Jug miniature	3"h	10-20			
5443	Jug miniature etched lines	3"h	10-20			
5444	Jug miniature 'Hollington' range		10-20			
5445	Jug miniature 'Hollington' range	3"h	10-20			
5446	Jug miniature 'Hollington' range	3"h	10-20			
5447	Honey pot 'Anniversary' range	5"h	5-10			
5448	Goblet 'Anniversary' range	5"h	8-12			
5449	Tea pot 'Anniversary' range		15-20			
5450	Plate 'Anniversary' range	10"dia	8-12			
5451	Trinket box 'Anniversary' range	4.5"l	8-12			
5452	Cream jug 'Anniversary' range		3-6			
5453	Tea cup 'Anniversary' range		2-5			
5454	Tea saucer 'Anniversary' range		1-2			
5455	Tea plate 'Anniversary' range	6.25"dia	5-10			
5456	Loving cup 'Anniversary' range		8-12			
5457	Bowl 'Anniversary' range		3-5			
5458	Ashtray 'Anniversary' range		2-4			
5459	Candle stick 'Anniversary' range	6.75"h	8-12			
5460	Bell 'Anniversary' range	5.25"h	10-15			
5461-5464	Not used					
5465	Egg cup chicken shape		5-10			
5466	Egg cup stand for four chickens		15-25			

Mould No	Description	Size	Price Guide in £'s	Colour	Date Purchased	Price Paid
5467	N/I					
5468	Cruet set 'Nessie'		30-50			
5469	Jug 'Hollington' range'	9"h	18-25			
5470	Jug with spout 'Hollington' range'	9"h	18-25			
5471	Jug 'Hollington' range'	9"h	18-25			
5472	Jug 'Hollington' range'	9"h	18-25			
5473	Jug 'Hollington' range'	6.5"h	10-20			
5474	Jug 'Hollington' range'	6.5"h	10-20			
5475	Jug 'Hollington' range'	6.5"h	10-20			
5476	Jug with spout 'Hollington' range'	6.5"h	10-20			
5477	Not used					
5478	Egg cup truck 'Nursery Ware' #		50-70			
5479	Egg cup steam engine 'Nursery Ware' #		50-70			
5480	Jam pot Teddy bear #		20-40			
5481	Vase hand painted 'High Tide' range	5.75"h	10-20			
5482	Bowl 'High Tide' range		10-20			
5483	Plant pot 'High Tide' range	4"h	12-18			
5484	Plant pot 'High Tide' range	5"h	15-20			
5485	Vase 'High Tide' range	7.75"h	15-20			
5486	Vase 'High Tide' range	4.5"h	8-12			
5487	Basket 'High Tide' range		10-15			
5488	Flower Holder 'High Tide' range	8.5"dia	10-15			
5489	Bowl 'High Tide' range	5.25"l	5-10			

Mould No	Description	Size	Price Guide in £'s	Colour	Date Purchased	Price Paid
5490	Vase Acorn		5-10			
5491	Vase		5-10			
5492	Vase		5-10			
5493	Vase		5-10			
5494	Vase		5-10			
5495-5498	Not used					
5499	Vase 'Autumn Leaves' range	6"h	5-10			
5500	Plant pot 'Autumn Leaves' range	6"h	5-10			
5501	Jug 'Autumn Leaves' range	8"h	10-15			
5502	Vase 'Autumn Leaves' range	10"h	12-18			
5503	Covered bowl on foot 'Autumn Leaves' range		8-12			
5504	Vase 'Autumn Leaves' range	11"l	5-10			
5505	Plant pot 'Autumn Leaves' range	5"h	8-12			
5506	Plant pot 'Autumn Leaves' range	7"h	15-20			
5507	Trinket box 'Autumn Leaves' range		8-12			
5508	Candle stick 'Autumn Leaves' range		5-10			
5509	Jug 'Autumn Leaves' range	7"h	10-15			
5510	Specimen vase		5-10			
5511	Specimen vase		5-10			
5512	Specimen vase 'Solo' range	4.25"h	5-10			
5513	Specimen vase 'Solo' range	6.25"h	8-12			
5514	Specimen vase 'Solo' range	4"h	5-10			
5515	Specimen vase 'Solo' range	6.25"h	8-12			

Mould No	Description	Size	Price Guide in £'s	Colour	Date Purchased	Price Paid
5516	Specimen vase 'Solo' corn cob	6.25"h	8-12			
5517	Brooch/pendant dog Retriever's head		20-35			
5518	Brooch/pendant dog Cairn's head		20-35			
5519	Brooch/pendant dog Poodle's head		20-35			
5520	Brooch/pendant dog Bulldog's head		20-35			
5521	Brooch/pendant dog Spaniel's head		20-35			
5522	Brooch/pendant dog Collie's head		20-35			
5523	Brooch/pendant horse's head		20-35			
5524	Brooch/pendant horse's head		20-35			
5525	Brooch/pendant horse's head		20-35			
5526-5528	Not used					
5529	Salt and pepper beer mugs		15-20			
5530	Money box beer mug		15-20			
5531	Salt full beer mug		10-15			
5532	Money box full beer mug		15-20			
5533	Pot	4"h	5-10			
5534	Not used					
5535	Bell 'Croft' range	4.75"h	8-12			
5536	Jug 'Croft' range	7"h	15-20			
5537	Coffee pot 'Croft' range	9"h	25-30			
5538	Clock 'Croft' range	8"w	25-35			
5539-5546	Not used					
5547	Honey pot clown		20-25			

Mould No	Description	Size	Price Guide in £'s	Colour	Date Purchased	Price Paid
5548	Vinegar bottle 'Nosey Parker' face	5.75"h	70-90			
5549	Pepper 'Nosey Parker' face	5"h	60-80			
5550	Salt 'Nosey Parker' face	4.75"h	60-80			
5551	Tray for plant pots		5-8			
5552	Tray for plant pots		5-8			
5553	Cradle	3.5"h	15-20			
5554	Pair of baby boots	3.5"h	15-20			
5555	Stork carrying bundle	4.5"h	15-20			
5556-5558	Not used					
5559	Wall plaque miniature	4.25"dia	10-15			
5560	Wall plaque miniature	3.5"dia	10-15			
5561-5562	Not used					
5563	Tray		8-10			
5564	Toilet roll holder		5-8			
5565	Covered jar for bath salts		10-15			
5566	Tooth brush holder		10-15			
5567	Bowl for dentures		10-15			
5568-5570	Not used					
5571	Plant pot 'Giant Panda' range	4.5"h	20-30			
5572	Twin vase 'Giant Panda' range	6.25"h	20-35			
5573	Jug 'Giant Panda' range	9"h	30-40			
5574	Jug 'Giant Panda' range	7.5"h	20-30			
5575	Bowl 'Giant Panda' range		20-30			

Mould No	Description	Size	Price Guide in £'s	Colour	Date Purchased	Price Paid
5576	Money box 'Giant Panda' range	4.25"h	30-40			
5577	Not used 'Giant Panda' range					
5578	Panda sitting 'Giant Panda' range	2.25"h	20-30			
5579	Panda standing 'Giant Panda' range	1.5"h	20-30			
5580	Disc small		10-15			
5581	Disc large		10-15			
5582	Martingale three discs on leather		20-25			
5583	Martingale three discs on leather		20-25			
5584	Trinket box 'Milady' range		8-12			
5585	Ring stand 'Milady' range		4-6			
5586	Plant pot 'Milady' range	6.75"dia	15-25			
5587	Tray 'Milady' range	10"l	5-10			
5588	Covered bowl 'Milady' range	4.5"dia	8-12			
5589	Candle stick 'Milady' range	4"h	4-6			
5590	Plant pot 'Milady' range	5.5"dia	15-20			
5591	Plant pot 'Milady' range	4.75"dia	12-18			
5592	Vase 'Milady' range	8"h	12-18			
5593	Vase 'Milady' range	6"h	8-12			
5594	Hand mirror 'Milady' range		10-15			
5595	Specimen vase 'Milady' range	6.75"h	8-12			
5596	Vase '1904' range	8.5"h	10-20			
5597	Jug '1904' range	9"h	10-20			
5598	Vase '1904' range	9.5"h	10-20			

Mould No	Description	Size	Price Guide in £'s	Colour	Date Purchased	Price Paid
5599	Vase '1904' range	9.25"h	10-20			
5600	Vase '1904' range	9"h	10-20			
5601-5605	Not used					
5606	Vase 'Belgravia' range	8.25"h	10-20			
5607	Vase 'Belgravia' range	6.75"h	10-15			
5608	Vase 'Belgravia' range	6"h	5-10			
5609	Vase 'Belgravia' range	6.25"l	5-10			
5610	Bowl 'Belgravia' range		8-12			
5611	Plant pot 'Belgravia' range	4.5"h	10-15			
5612	Plant pot 'Belgravia' range	5"h	10-15			
5613	Plant pot 'Belgravia' range	5.5"h	12-18			
5614	Plant pot 'Belgravia' range	6.5"h	15-20			
5615	Plant pot 'Belgravia' range	7.5"h	15-25			
5616-5619	Not used					
5620	Tea cup 'Tapestry' range		3-5			
5621	Tea saucer 'Tapestry' range		1-2			
5622	Tea plate 'Tapestry' range	6.5"dia	4-6			
5623	Mug 'Tapestry' range	4.5"h	4-8			
5624	Sugar bowl 'Tapestry' range		3-5			
5625	Cream jug 'Tapestry' range		4-8			
5626	Tea pot 'Tapestry' range	5"h	15-20			
5627	Sandwich tray 'Tapestry' range	11.75"l	5-8			
5628	Salt and pepper 'Tapestry' range		8-12			

Mould No	Description	Size	Price Guide in £'s	Colour	Date Purchased	Price Paid
5629	Butter dish 'Tapestry' range		12-20			
5630	Cheese dish 'Tapestry' range		12-20			
5631	Preserve pot 'Tapestry' range	3.5"h	8-10			
5632-5633	Not used					
5634	Tea pot large		20-25			
5635	Tea pot large		20-25			
5636	Tea pot small		15-20			
5637	Tea pot small		15-20			
5638-5643	Not used					
5644	Thimble wedding cake ,with box		20-25			
5645-5654	Not used					
5655	Mug pig		10-15			
5656	Money box bear	5.25"h	30-40			
5657	Money box pig	5.5"h	30-40			
5658	Money box rabbit	5.75"h	30-40			
5659	Money box elephant	5.75"h	35-45			
5660	Money box Cheshire cat	6.25"l	35-45			
5661	Money box Bassett hound	5.5"h	30-40			
5662	Money box fish	6.5"l	40-50			
5663-5669	Not used					
5670	Tea pot 'Tudor Cottage' range		20-35			
5671	Sugar bowl 'Tudor Cottage' range		15-20			
5672	Cream jug 'Tudor Cottage' range		15-20			

Mould No	Description	Size	Price Guide in £'s	Colour	Date Purchased	Price Paid
5673	Butter dish 'Tudor Cottage' range		25-30			
5674	Cheese dish 'Tudor Cottage' range		25-30			
5675	Preserve pot 'Tudor Cottage' range	4.5"h	20-30			
5676	Salt and pepper 'Tudor Cottage' range		15-25			
5677-5995	Not used					
5996	Newspaper holder 'Desk Top' range	4.5"h	20-25			
5997	Match box tray 'Desk Top' range		15-20			
5998	Match box pen holder 'Desk Top' range		15-20			
5999	Sack pen holder 'Desk Top' range		20-25			
6000	Scrap paper tray 'Desk Top' range		20-25			
6001	Box gift wrapped 'Desk Top' range		10-20			
6002	Carrier bag pen holder 'Desk Top' range		8-15			
6002	Carrier bag pen holder for Harrods		20-25			
6003	Money box parcel 'Desk Top' range		15-20			
6004	Paper weight 'Desk Top' range		15-20			
6005	Ball of string dispenser 'Desk Top' range		15-20			
6006	Beer can		15-20			
6007-6127	Not used					
6128	Money box letter 'P'		20-25			

FACTORY CEASED PRODUCTION

Particular patterns decorated on 'Avon' shapes will command higher prices. For example nursery ware: Zoo line, Teddy.

Mould No	Description	Size	Price Guide in £'s	Colour	Date Purchased	Price Paid
3262	Plate	8"dia	10-16			
3263	Plate	6.5"dia	8-12			
3264	Bowl	6.25"dia	10-14			
3617	Baby mug 2 handle		20-30			
3742	Mug		15-25			
3788	Egg cup		10-15			
3791	Baby plate		15-20			
5478	Egg cup engine trailer		15-70			
5479	Engine		50-70			
5480	Jam pot teddy bear		20-40			

The SylvaC Collectors Handbook Part 1 & 2 are only the briefest of guides. Part 1 covers mould numbers 1-300, Part 2 3001-6128. Published by Georgian Publications PO Box 1449, Bath, BA1 2FF.

Further reading:

Shaw & Copestake The Collectors Guide to Early SylvaC 1894-1939 by Anthony Van Der Woerd, published by Georgian Publications, PO Box 1449, Bath, BA1 2FF

The SylvaC Story, The SylvaC Companion and The Falcon Ware Story all by Susan Jean Verbeek and published by Pottery Publications, 7 Merton Park Parade, Kingston Road, London SW19 3NT.